KANCI
WH

Rea Oberoi is a hotelier by birth and a mountain girl
by birth and choice. She is the daughter of the late Brij
Raj 'Diamond' Oberoi, who was the nephew of the father
of the Indian Hotel Industry—M.S. Oberoi. Her debut
book gives you a glimpse of life in the Himalayan abodes
of Darjeeling and Sikkim, especially the Elgin group of
hotels.

www.elginhotels.com
https://instagram.com/elginhotels

KANCHENJUNGA WHISPERS

WHISPERS

Legends and Tales from The Elgin

REA OBEROI

RUPA

Published by
Rupa Publications India Pvt. Ltd 2023
7/16, Ansari Road, Daryaganj
New Delhi 110002

Sales centres:
Bengaluru Chennai
Hyderabad Jaipur Kathmandu
Kolkata Mumbai Prayagraj

P-ISBN: 978-93-5702-657-4
E-ISBN: 978-93-5702-754-0

First impression 2023

10 9 8 7 6 5 4 3 2 1

The moral right of the author has been asserted.

Printed in India

My hotel is my home
comprising stories of all the people living within.

Inspired by real events and personal experiences,
I dedicate this to my creator,
the immortal mountains and my mortal masters.

CONTENTS

1

THE ELGIN

Nestled in the Himalayas stands a dollhouse-like structure in the quaint town of Darjeeling. The journey from the flatlands of Bengal up the twisting mountain roads surrounded by tea estates and through virgin forests takes the visitor to the golden gates of The Elgin Hotel.

The smell of Mother Earth gushes through my car's open windows, carried in by the blowing wind that is playing with my long raven hair. Each time the wind tickles me with its cold breath and brushes past my chin, I sense a tingle in my ears while my emerald dangler earrings caress my face. The Himalayan mist engulfs me as my car climbs up the mountains. Tiny water droplets settle on my eyelashes as I close my eyes, rest my head against the window frame and feel the Himalayan breeze stroking my forehead. 'Hello, my love!' it seems to say in this intimate moment, 'Hold me in your arms, for I have been longing to be with you.'

I get out of my car and step onto the large petals of red poinsettias lying on the ground. The Himalayan winds waltz around me like a lover waiting impatiently to hold their love in their strong arms, which makes me succumb again to its charm.

I walk towards the reception through the Duchess Garden, a green expanse lined with rows of bright yellow marigolds and rainbow hues of rare Himalayan orchids. I am surrounded by nature's exuberance with every step that I take and sense a divine presence in the air. 'Indra! The God of thunder. I feel you around me. Your chiselled arms, sculpted in these mountains, beckon me, and now I have returned to the "land of the king of the Gods", I quietly speak to the divine presence as Lord Indra's mysterious aura captivates me and the sky turns ultramarine. 'Have you missed me too?' I whisper to the immortals.

The silence is suddenly broken with the greeting barks of my two fluffy Russian Samoyeds, Peter and Lilian. They come pouncing and tumbling over each other to welcome me. In fact, as soon as my car entered the hotel premises, my snowballs sensed my arrival—and began wagging their tails in excitement, staring patiently but directly at the towering gates even before the guards themselves were alerted. Lilian looks up at me with her doe-like eyes, full of compassion. Her eyes resemble mine, as though lined with charcoal. How ladylike my Lilian is! I hold her in my arms, her pink paws dangling over my shoulders as we touch our foreheads.

'My babies! How I longed for you two!' I express my love out loud, taking the gloves off my hands to feel their soft fur running through my fingers. Lilian smells of fresh rosemary— straight out of her warm bath. In the company of my Samoyeds, I feel like I can truly breathe again.

The changing season is clearly visible in Darjeeling's panorama, providing an optical journey for my visually inclined mind. November is here, and the hotel is decorated with oil lamps and candles, whether hanging within lanterns from the branches of tall trees or floating on waterbeds, replicating the stars of distant galaxies. The creative flower decorations are a sight for sore eyes. The 'festival of lights' brightens up the heritage hotel in its golden hues. The Elgin was once a summer palace of the Maharaja of Cooch

Behar, later revamped into a heritage hotel, followed by the development of the brand of 'Elgin Hotels and Resorts' by our very own king of hospitality, Mr B.R. Oberoi (popularly known as Diamond)—my father.

I close my charcoal eyes and breathe in the woodsy aroma lingering in the winter air. The whiff of sandalwood connects me to the very essence of my being. In the distance, I see my mother, Nimmi, lighting the first diya to welcome Goddess Lakshmi into our home. She is delicately placing the diya on a thali decorated with silver coins. She is the Lakshmi or the lady luck of our house, walking gracefully in the garden while her pashmina shawl glides behind her like the cloak of an empress.

An effortless smile appears on my face, accompanied by teardrops of yearning that run down my cheeks. I feel a wave of emotions overpowering me, like a gushing Himalayan waterfall. Shifting, whistling winds and a variety of exquisite Himalayan flowers greet me as I wipe away my tears of joy. A familiar voice calls out as I enter the wooden double doors. 'Cherry brandy, anyone?'

Cherry brandy is the welcome drink offered at the hotel. It fills each guest with a sense of warmth in the crisp, cold air of Darjeeling. The signature drink is offered to me as well, along with a white silk scarf that is draped around my shoulders by Prashant, the doorman. The Elgin is not just any hotel; it is my home. I wait for my elder sister Aanyaa—my north star—with the rest of my family. I see Mr Diamond, the rock of our house, strolling through the gates of The Elgin with my head governess Jethi, Mr Butler, Mr Dorjee (the driver) and Mr Neeru (the night guard). I walk into the hotel to sit by the blazing fireplace and soon feeling returns to my numb toes. The cosy environment of the lobby with its Italian crystal chandeliers, deep plum carpets and wooden inner décor lends a perfect blend of luxury, relaxation and romance.

'Welcome home, Madam. A very happy Diwali to you!' the general manager says to me. 'Thank you, Badal! It's good to be back,' I say, reciprocating with a smile, and shake his hand softly but steadily. Gazing at the dancing flame within the intricately carved fireplace, I relax on the blue velvet couch. It is a tiring road trip up the mountain's steep bends, and the toasty environment is making me drowsy, especially with the sight of the mellow sunset. With drooping eyes and flushed cheeks, I look through the lobby's pearly white windows to see the majestic Kanchenjunga gracefully standing amongst the fluffy clouds.

My eyes are locked on the beautiful scene as the blue evening sky changes to a crimson hue. A cold breeze teases me, making the black ribbon shoulder straps of my dress flutter. I feel a longing to dissolve into the mountain's lap. How I have longed for this! My gaze shifts towards the Himalayan golden eagles gliding through the sky, like two lovers embracing each other mid-flight. 'My sweet Darjeeling! How I longed for you...'

The floral aroma of tea floats freely, being carried by the unpredictable wind, as we are surrounded by countless tea estates. The smell of the first flush (the first tea that is harvested in spring, or even late winter) brewing in the kitchen is a clear sign that I have finally come home.

Patria est ubi cor est. Home is where the heart is.

∽

It is 10 a.m. the next day when my doorbell rings; I wake up to a loud but polite voice. 'Good morning, Rea Madam!' In comes my housekeeper—full of energy, performing her morning chores, starting with serving me breakfast in bed (an assorted fruit platter). She makes the lilac curtains go whoosh…and binds them with golden tassels.

Oh no! says the voice in my head as the large French windows give way to the direct rays of the bright morning sun that reaches my eyes through the thin canopy of my bed. Leaving the warmth of my Egyptian cotton linen with an electric blanket tucked under the sheets is one hell of a task in this cold.

I pick up my phone from the wooden bedside table and dial '9' for the reception. I prefer to call reception directly instead of room service, a habit I developed in childhood. At that very moment, I could hear the sound of stilettos tapping on the wooden floors, reaching into my bedroom. I put the phone down. My mother arrives, deep in conversation with the head housekeeper, Kailie.

Standing directly in the path of the morning rays, my mother stares straight at me while the Sri Lankan sapphires adorning her strands of dark brown hair with coffee-coloured highlights glint a prismatic blue. She walks gracefully towards my bed and sits down right next to me. With her ice-cold hand on my cheek, she gives me a warm cuddle. The scent of her skin and the soft sweater on my face is what home is all about. My mother glances at her wristwatch, with a mother-of-pearl dial—it is 10.10 a.m. 'This synchronicity is insistent on following me wherever I go. The time is almost like a mirror of double digits. This morning I woke up at 06.06 a.m.' Mama says, in love with her binary world. Further, she insists that I drink tea without any milk or sugar. 'Rise and shine, Rea! Darjeeling tea is the best in the world and we are blessed to have it growing all around us,' she says with pride. 'We are from Darjeeling after all. We must drink tea in the proper fashion. Besides, it works wonders for your metabolism and skin, and also your mood.' I drift into misery though at the thought of having black tea, pulling the thick bedcovers over my head.

My mother takes the quality of her tea very seriously. I giggle from under the covers as she leaves my bedroom in a hurry with a list of events planned out for the day. Mama leaves a trail of peppermint and patchouli scents in my room, making my taste buds tingle, which leads me to order the good old-fashioned Indian tea. 'One masala chai, please. Oh, and one scrambled egg to go with it!' This time, I ring room service instead because I know my mother is headed straight for the reception. I am well acquainted with the fresh aroma of the first flush, with a slice of ginger dissolved in it and puffed rice sprinkled on top. This is my special in-house tea ritual, hiding behind the doors of my room, away from my parents' eyes.

My mother once caught me red-handed with masala chai and yelled into the long corridors. 'No! Not this ginger tea!'

Reminded of that incident, I further say, 'Let's keep this between ourselves, shall we, Badal? Mama will cancel my order if she gets a whiff of it. But I need my morning boost before I start my day. Oh…and a quick reminder! Are the mountain bikes ready? Aanyaa and I will be down in thirty.' After leaving the general manager with my instructions, I laze around in my room for a couple of minutes before getting ready for the day. None of us leaves the confines of our bedrooms without being dressed elegantly from head to toe—a mandatory drill for us hoteliers. To be seen in our pyjamas would induce multiple strokes among the staff. My father, a seasoned hotelier, says, 'I cannot understand people when they have two piles of clothes in their wardrobe—one called "home clothes" and the other "outdoor clothes". I could barely recognize an associate of mine when I bumped into him on his porch. He was wearing a

grey sweater and pyjamas with holes! Why would he do that?'
With the dress code right, I head out of my cottage-like suite
to make my way down the long corridor, all the way to the
ground floor. I live in the topmost section of the hotel, on the
fifth floor, which gives me some private space. My room has
a 360-degree view of the mountains, and is made entirely of
Bhutanese wood with powder blue upholstery enhancing its
décor—a combination my mother adores; she makes sure that
each room is personally designed. 'Our hotel is our home,' she
says, and my mother surely works her charm—with my father
in the background, saying, 'Rome wasn't built in a day!' This
is our special recipe. Home-grown and completely organic.

'Good morning! Yes, a good day to you too!' I keep
nodding, wishing every familiar staff member and unknown
guest as I make my way down the labyrinth of stairs through
the corridors. It is a mandatory code of conduct if your hotel
is your home. Displaying good manners is right at the top
when it comes to being a good host, especially a good leader.
This is the way I have grown up. It is our style statement.

For many people, homes are private spaces, where they
can let their hair down, but for me, it is quite a challenge to
maintain privacy in a house full of guests I barely know, and
who keep changing on a regular basis. But there's an underlying
beauty to it. It is absolutely unusual…and I have come to love
the unusual. My friends have neighbours and live within a
colony while I have strange guests and a brilliant concierge.
It can sometimes be entertaining, and at other times, leave
a tinge of loneliness that lines the corners of this glamorous
frame. My life is a cocktail of sprinkled chillies, with a sour
twist at the top—more on the lines of a delicious Bloody Mary
and a whisky sour combined. The two intertwine to create a
unique essence. No words, no actions are needed to describe

this feeling any further. Just a single sniff of the aroma expands your senses, creating an unexplainable touch of happiness, thereby satisfying the soul and sumptuously filling the stomach with the experiences on your plate.

2

MR DIAMOND

My mother lovingly calls Mr Diamond 'Head Gardener' because of his talent for landscape gardening. He spends more time outdoors than indoors. 'Mama, have you seen Papa? I have been looking all over for him,' I say, pacing up and down my attic room. My mother, resplendent in white cashmere while solving her favourite sudoku puzzle, says, 'Rea, you know where to find him. He prefers the fresh air of the outdoors to being confined within the four walls. Our "Head Gardener" is in his element. Look outside the window.' While my mother thrives on solving riddles, living amongst Mother Nature is Mr Diamond's way of life. Landscaping is his forte, and if you glance at The Elgin's gardens, you will know exactly what I mean.

I look out the window to see him standing in the Garden of Eden, where I go for a walk with him every day. I feel carefree in these moments that we spend together; it is our father–daughter time.

'There you are, Papa!' I exclaim, emerging from the corner, dodging a large oil burner in the garden. I see him standing somewhere among his precious Himalayan orchids. I move downhill through the many stone pathways that extend into the green lawns. Mr Diamond is brilliant at artistic landscaping and creating something extraordinary and absolutely out of this world. I walk through the paradise he painstakingly created and admire his flower babies. With a watering can in hand, I follow his footsteps, pouring water on the bountiful bird-of-paradise flowers, hydrangeas, daffodils, pink petunias, tiger lilies, large round marigolds and the dandelions dancing amidst the manicured lawns. The strong aromas of these flowers envelop me as a cold Himalayan breeze starts to blow.

The tall bougainvillea and rhododendron trees, seemingly reaching for the heavens, enhance The Elgin's charm. My father has developed five such properties that are spread out in the Northeastern Himalayas in West Bengal and Sikkim. Each one is an architectural marvel. It's hard to choose my favourite among them because they all mean home to me, each having a personality of its own. My father often says, 'My darling, it's much like the five fingers of your hand. Each one is necessary as each performs a distinct function. The five come together to form a powerful fist; our organization is just like this fist. It is one big family and we are the binding threads of its magic.'

Our hotels are beautifully landscaped, personally designed and reconstructed by Mr Diamond with love and unwavering commitment. Reviving heritage properties is of utmost importance to my father, who aims to not only add value and luxury but also to preserve the remnants of a bygone era. Living the magic he has created in the resorts is an experience of a lifetime. He says, 'These old palaces must be revamped from time to time, for it is my calling to preserve their history. I feel the properties have chosen me to be their caretaker. I feel a strong connection to them. It's love at first sight!' My father often says, *Ars longa, vita brevis*. Art is long, life is short.

During dusk, I can smell the sweet roses, lavender and lilies in the Duchess Garden, which transports me to another dimension. I shift my gaze towards the elderflower and ask for my father's permission to take an orchid along with me to put in a vase in my bedroom. Mr Diamond's reply immediately follows in a serious yet soft tone, 'Rea, do not pick flowers at odd hours or around sunset.'

'Why, Papa?' I ask with curiosity.

'My dear, flowers are mysterious elements of nature. You surely know about their magical essence, don't you? Flowers are home to fairies. Their delicate petals are where the fairies sleep at night. Flowers breathe. They feel and sense everything. Just like us humans, they too are living beings. Flowers too feel pleasure and pain, Rea. You should admire them in the garden; if you pick the flowers, they will wither away and the beauty of the blossoms will fade.'

His words of wisdom have always filled my life with light since the very beginning. Our conversation continues as we sit in the gazebo, enjoying our customary high tea. An assortment of sandwiches and scones laden with fresh farm cream, homemade butter and strawberry jam are on the menu. I can feel the soft white butter melting in my mouth. The sun begins to set, shying away behind the Himalayas, which signals the arrival of 'fairies'—a swarm of fireflies that illuminate the branches of the surrounding trees, flying around the Duchess Garden. And this is how Papa connects us to nature with his meaningful stories. Mother Nature is sacred to him, and now it is to me too.

Born on a full moon night, my father's intuitive skills are extraordinary, along with his sensitivity towards nature. Mr Diamond was born in November, and water being his ruling sign, he possesses a high level of creativity, empathy and telepathy. He always seems to know if something unusual is coming his way and tends to avoid that path altogether. He says, 'Avoid danger, my darling. There is no need to go crashing into the eye of the storm unless it is absolutely necessary. Especially where my daughters are concerned.'

Like a full moon brightens the darkest of nights, he has the natural quality of shining through even during the darkest periods of our lives. My mother has a famous saying about my father, *Allis volat propriis*. He flies with his own wings.

My father was given the nickname 'Diamond' by his uncle, M.S. Oberoi, the founder of the Oberoi group of hotels. According to him, at first sight, my father's eyes glimmered like two tiny diamonds as he gazed up from my grandmother's arms.

Mr Diamond is an excellent judge of character, which makes him the best man for the job when it comes to recruiting people. 'My dear, I am carved through experience. I can tell if a person is up for the job within five minutes of interviewing them. For years, I have been interacting with all sorts of people. It has sharpened my skills of recognizing a man's intent and nature within minutes,' he says, while sipping on a cup of hot Darjeeling tea.

He is very particular about his daily routine. Each morning, the breakfast trolley is rolled into his bedchamber with an assortment of food. He relishes having his two poached eggs and brown toast, freshly squeezed Darjeeling orange juice, along with his favourite item on the menu—porridge topped with hot milk, served in the finest crockery. The porridge remains a constant, despite a change in his choice of eggs each morning.

Red and white chequered napkins are tidily laid out. The general manager stands next to him and checks all the boxes, giving him his daily itinerary; all instructions regarding what should be done in the hotels are simultaneously given to the general manager. A heap of chequebooks and cheesecake surround my father. At times, he too wears a cheesy smile.

The telephone ringing off the hook and all the general managers of the hotels taking instructions from him is a common sight. I often hear my mother say, 'Diamond, put your phone on silent. I cannot function with the constant ringing. Why does everyone call you directly for the smallest inconvenience? I can hear your phone ringing in my ears even when you are not around. Please limit your phone to office hours.'

My father, nevertheless, picks up his call and addresses my mother softly. 'Office hours? There is no such thing as office hours for hoteliers. We work round the clock, Nimmi. You know it. I need to know what is going on in all the hotels. What if there is an emergency and I avoid the call? You will surely blame me for it later. This is also the reason why the kids call me first. They say, "Papa, you are the perfect person to contact in the case of an emergency. Mama never picks up. She is always leaving her phone plugged in somewhere."' He slyly puts the message across and leaves my mother speechless, returning to his conversation with the general managers.

My father has a uniquely organized and centralized way of working. Not even a single spoon can go missing from the hotels without his knowledge. He demands perfection at all The Elgin properties when it comes to brand value and service. Each of our departments exudes elegance and bears a personal touch. He is the field marshal to his generals.

As Aanyaa and I walk through the corridors with him while performing our daily checks, my father reminds us, 'My darlings, always remember that work never stops in a hotel. We are constantly evolving and changing things with the new tide. So do not be disheartened when you see a dent or two on the roof. Keep calm and think of a solution. Just call the carpenters and give wings to your creativity.' This is our little secret to running a hotel.

I watch him check each room personally, switching the lights on and off, fixing even the slightest tilt on a photo frame. After all, he is not just our father. His hotels are like his children. Mr Diamond puts in an equal amount of care for his concrete children as he does for us three siblings—me, Aanyaa and our brother Viraj. My father lovingly tells us, 'I wish to enhance my experiences here on earth to lead a meaningful existence. My way of life is a merger of my passion for hotels and my tight-knit family. Whatever you choose to do, my darlings, do it with your heart and it will manifest into something magical.'

There is more to my father than what meets the eye. A secret not many people know. Not even his closest friends. Mr Diamond's real name is used only on official occasions and it has a more powerful ring to it. My grandmother Shanti Oberoi named him Brij Raj. I recall my grandmother tantalizing our taste buds with hot halwa on the auspicious day of Guru Purnima, which happened to coincide with my father's birthday that year. In her comforting voice, she said, 'Brij Raj is another name for the Hindu God Krishna, who is an avatar of Lord Vishnu.' Seated on the floor of our mandir, my grandmother took us into her world. Our household has always been devoted to Lord Vishnu, and so, she named her youngest of six children Brij Raj.

I personally adore the name Diamond. Aanyaa's and my eyes twinkle when we hear strangers addressing us in public. 'Hello, my dears! You are Diamond's daughters, aren't you?' I instantly feel special as the voice of my angel, Michael, rings in my ears. 'Shine in your truest form—because you're Diamond's daughters.'

My eyes glaze over as I think about Mr Diamond's life. I see him dressed every day in a bespoke suit, complete with a tie and a matching silk pocket square. While I get back to the chilling scene in the novel I'm reading, I wait for him by the fireplace while he usually takes a few more minutes to dab on his cologne and comb his thick dark hair. No one dared interfere in that department. My father makes his point quite clear to all of us in the house by saying, 'I am the only sibling with thick hair. The rest of my brothers are bald. I need to take care of my precious hair.'

Having donned a coral cashmere sweater, I welcome the frosty mornings. The tip of my nose is cherry red, and it is getting colder still, so I move closer to the fire. With my head down and my nose in the book, I notice in my peripheral vision a pair of shiny leather shoes pointing right at me.

'Good morning, my darling. What are you reading there? You seem lost in its pages. Hmm… *The Last Queen*? Sounds interesting. My little queen is enjoying it, I see. Tell me all about it at dinner. Well, Rea, I have a meeting in the next ten minutes. Could you please help me with this?'

I see him struggling with an exquisite tie pin in his hand. It is shaped like a swan and is encrusted with neatly placed diamonds. I have a sudden urge to borrow it from him. The miniature swan is absolutely stunning.

'Good morning, Papa. Well, you are certainly dressed to impress! How can the meeting go wrong when you have such beautiful accessories to accompany you?' I giggle and place the diamond swan at the centre of his tie.

'Now you are ready to dazzle the conference hall, Papa. Oh! Wait a minute. What about the cufflinks? How I love selecting those for you. You mustn't forget the cufflinks. Specifically the ones with the engraved monogram "D". Do you know which ones I am talking about? The rose gold cufflinks, Papa. Customized specially by Mama to match your distinct personality.'

While I explore my favourite section of the wooden chest with its selection of customized cufflinks and antique pens, my father reaches for his black cashmere overcoat to head downstairs to the hotel lobby where he begins his busy day. He exudes confidence, which comes straight from his vast knowledge of art, architecture, design, décor, history, politics, botany, sustainability, his views on life, refined mannerisms, polite behaviour, his outward attire and most of all, his faith in magic and the divine.

He gives me the warmest of hugs and his gentle kiss on my forehead seems to bring in the sun. My father's hands are as soft as a feather's touch and my face melts in his hands. 'Rea, I hope you are ready for the grand soirée. It will be followed by a candlelight dinner, and Mama's special chocolate soufflé is on the menu.' Later, as the moon peeps out, my mother puts forward a question to him in good humour while hosting the dinner party, 'My love, when will you get me a lovely diamond? I am still waiting for one.'

Papa raises himself from his seat and replies, holding her hands softly, 'Here, Nimmi. You have the biggest diamond of them all.' His words shift the mood in the room and everyone bursts out laughing, which carries itself throughout the dinner table. Although Mr Diamond is the boss, the keys to the vault lie with my mother. He enjoys it, no doubt.

He does not hesitate to shower us with compliments on every occasion. To me, he says, 'My girls always look lovely, especially if they are happy and have a smile on their faces. A natural glow no one can take away.' My sister and I break into waves of laughter and nudge each other while whispering to him. 'Papa, this is the dress you said was not worth buying.' He then immediately reacts, 'Of course not, darling! I don't recollect saying such a thing. It's a beautiful dress and looks even better on you...'

I guess he may be right, but it is his best way of getting away with the million-dollar question. How gracefully he denies every uncomfortable thing. Being surrounded by so many women in the house—my mother and two daughters—does not make things easy for him. My brother Viraj, in contrast, is smart, and dares not interfere in matters of women and fashion.

My father likes to take credit for every other thing, including the strong family genes that he has passed on to us. The Oberoi genes are very evident; the whole clan walks around with sharp features, especially the patent 'Oberoi nose'.

My father is a perfect boss, a loving husband and most of all, a remarkable parent. Everyone who he comes in touch with usually loves him and feels at home in his presence. Mr Diamond always has a smile on his face and a twinkle in his eyes.

'Mama, don't you think he possesses a larger-than-life image? His charm carries to the ends of any room he walks into. How lucky you are to have this in a man! He is patient as well. A rare find in my generation.' I tell my mother as I seek my own diamond in the dust.

'Yes, I'm certain you will say this, Rea, as you're your father's favourite. You get away with anything! His delicate little "Shona". Our youngest occupies a special place in Papa's heart.'

When it comes to public relations, my parents are brilliant hosts. The Elgin has the most extraordinary celebrations in its grand hall thanks to this duo. The chandeliers light up its high ceilings, the wooden floor shines as I walk on it and the wide staircases connecting the hotel's public spaces echo with the tunes of the grand piano in the Duke Hall. Its sweet melody takes over my senses. The smells of the chocolate chip cookies and butter croissants being baked in the kitchen are enticing.

The strong perfume worn by my father leaves a trail around The Elgin, making it *home*; soft velvet curtains are held together with golden tassels and the blazing fireplaces emit a red hue, which adds to its elegant décor. I feel the Victorian era open its doors, guiding me into a time of romantic gestures and of knights. I feel an urge to seek my handsome dark knight on my quest for true love.

My mother has brilliant taste in décor, transforming our hotels into our cosy homes. Pastel hues of the upholstery, a variety of Persian carpets on the wooden floors, the decorations on the walls and every piece of furniture are personally chosen, placed and designed by my mother. She puts her soul into her creations. With a graceful glance, my mother says to us, 'My dears, your home is a reflection of your personality. It is where you spend most of your time. It should have a personal touch and a welcoming ambience. This is the reason I do up the hotels myself. A hired designer cannot bring to life how I envision my home. After all my efforts, when I see the final outcome, I cannot tell you how satisfied and blissful it makes me feel.' We are indeed lucky that our mother is an electronic engineer *and* an interior decorator. An extremely rare combination. Her taste is surely unmatched by anyone else in the family and so is her demeanour.

While my mother walks towards the powder room, I take a walk around the public areas, admiring the ambience, and end up in the library where my father is hosting some of his guests. Seated on a hazel Chesterfield sofa, I hear him speak freely in this chamber of bound antiquarian books. The windows are latched up while the bukhari blazes in the corner; the library smells of charcoal and candlestick.

'What is everywhere yet is nowhere? Does anyone have the answer to my riddle?' Mr Diamond heats up the boiling pot of questions in the library. While everyone is scratching their heads, I answer, 'Uhm...is it space?' My father shakes his head and says, 'A confused mind.'

Giggling at my father's joke, I head to the Duke ballroom for a dance, hoping to find someone handsome to twirl with into the starry night.

3

A GUEST IN MY OWN HOUSE

The downside of having too many homes is having no permanent home at all. The excerpt from *The Rime of the Ancient Mariner* perfectly fits this situation, *Water, water, everywhere, nor any drop to drink*. Because our residence is within the hotel premises, having the same room for more than a week is highly unlikely. There are many aspects that lead us to shift base from one room to another, sometimes from one hotel to another too—either out of choice or compulsion, whether we like it or not. No one can live out of a suitcase better than us. Additionally, we have a wardrobe full of clothes in all five hotels—just in case. 'Why keep all eggs in one basket?' My father says. But the nightmare begins when I cannot find what I need at that moment.

For the weekend, Aanyaa and I are off to a marvellous tea estate, an hour away from Darjeeling. We stay at the estate, enjoy its tranquillity and sip green tea cocktails while appreciating the rolling tea gardens spread out as far as one can see. I can smell the tea leaves in the air—an earthy and floral scent. Nature's craftsmanship in the form of pink cherry blossoms and white magnolias dotting the tea gardens captivates me. Darjeeling is the land of tea and towering peaks.

'Isn't it amazing, Aanyaa? As much as I love everyone working with us, I also love the occasional freedom of being away from all staff members keeping their watchful eyes on us at all times. Not to forget the presence of all the hotel guests around us. We can finally let our hair down.'

'Oh yes, sweet freedom!' my sister says, looking at Kanchenjunga accompanied by the gushing river beneath. 'Aanyaa, I'm impressed by the countless streams that bless this Himalayan valley; they're wild, yet tamed, just like us.' I nudge my sister. Our bliss is about to be cut short though, by the setting sun, as the afternoon makes way for the evening. We hop into our car and find our way back home to Darjeeling.

'Welcome home, Madams! Can I take your overcoats? Have a good evening ahead.' The doorman, taking off his long black hat, welcomes us with a smile. 'Thank you, Prashant. We are happy to be back,' I reply.

'We are back in the Antarctic instead of the Himalayas!' my sister whispers to me, cracking one of her notorious jokes. Meanwhile, the bellboy arrives, looking smart in his uniform. We enter the cosy reception in a very jolly mood, which is warm because of the bukhari.

'My room keys, please,' I ask the receptionist while taking my handbag off my shoulder. Panic flares in her eyes and she tries to say, 'Madam, actually... Uh...,' she hesitates. I could sense something was wrong.

'Hello, Mademoiselles!' Badal, the general manager, swiftly enters the conversation. He brings with him a little more than his French. 'I regret to tell you that your room has been allocated to a guest.'

'A guest! All of a sudden? Why is that?' my sister enquires. Badal replies, 'There has been an overbooking, Madam. A group of young adults who have come to film a documentary required twenty rooms, whereas their travel agent made the mistake of booking only nineteen. The guests have arrived all the way from France. If we had not allocated them your room, the entire group booking would have been cancelled. Madam, we needed to accommodate them to prove that our hospitality is unmatched, even if their travel agent made a mistake.'

Well, while we are not too happy about it, what with being tired after a long day of sightseeing, we understand the situation—*Atithi devo bhava*, a guest is akin to God, and they always come first. Our general manager is nothing if not efficient as he immediately sets Plan B in motion. We are to stay with our father, in the drawing room of his suite. But alas, our belongings are locked up in a suitcase in the spare cupboard of our room, where the guests are now staying.

As soon as we reach Mr Diamond's suite, the wooden bathroom door opens. I see our father is busy with his shaving kit. Standing tall in navy blue checked pyjamas and warm bathroom slippers, we see him humming away to glory, white foam all over his face, the smell of vanilla and mint suspended in the air.

We walk towards our bathroom singer and see Lilian's curved white tail popping out from under the sink. She is curled up under my father's feet like a round cotton ball. 'Welcome, girls! I'm glad you remembered my teaching, *non ducor duco* (I am not led, I lead).' Our father tends to fling his Latin phrases at us from time to time. 'The entire hotel is our home. We have abundant rooms here, which are all at our disposal. Having a guest in one of our rooms for a few days will only teach us how to share our belongings and be more accommodating. You are young hoteliers and will need to manage a few hiccups here and there. My darlings, it is a temporary arrangement. Plus, it means that you get to stay with me and spend some more time with your Papa. What else could I ask for?' He always puts things across so gently that we are swept away in his sweet words and treat this situation like one big indoor picnic.

'Rea, while I do understand the circumstances, I have a different plan for the next time something like this happens. We will give Papa's room to the guest instead and act like we don't know a thing. We'll turn the tables,' jokes my sister as she tucks herself under her warm blanket. Lilian comes closer to cuddle next to us. Her warm white fur is as soft as a fluffy blanket in this cold. 'That is a solid plan. Good night, Aanyaa.'

Switching off our bedside lamp leaves just the blazing scarlet hue from the fireplace and two dancing cherubs placed atop it to give us company through the night.

4

HERE COMES THE NANNY

Our nanny has an unusual personality, which flits between that of the classic fairy godmother and a dictator. She may be petite but the fire in her eyes and her stern personality makes even the general manager quake in his boots. Her name is Ankhphutti Sherpa but we call her Jethi. The word 'Jethi' in Nepalese translates to the eldest female in the house—so it suits her perfectly. She is our 'Head Governess'—a title she gave herself because she likes playing the role of a supreme commander in our lives. She has her priorities in order. Walking around The Elgin with a straight posture and rough hands, she is a storm you don't want to get caught in.

Jethi is driven purely by her faith in Tibetan Buddhism; she is a woman of discipline and prayer. All of us at the hotel share an inside joke that Jethi is a reincarnated army commander—always ready for action. After all, Buddhism does believe in rebirth. She only gives me a crooked smile, shrugs her shoulders and replies, 'Well, maybe. One can only wonder.'

Despite no binding blood tie, she has an unbreakable soul connection with our family. Jethi's timing magically aligned with ours as she arrived a day before my brother—the eldest of us siblings—was born. 20 November 1981. That was the day our governess came to The Elgin and gradually became a pillar of strength in our lives. My mother claims to be more attached to Jethi than any of us, which is a never-ending argument. She says, 'Jethi is an angel sent down from the heavens, especially for me. I cannot imagine a moment without her.' It has proved to be true as Jethi has lived with us ever since; never taking a single day off. 'This is my home,' she says. 'I don't need a holiday from home.' Jethi laughs then and heads upstairs to her private pantry for some hot Tibetan tea. Her powerful personality is unlike that of any other human being I have come in contact with.

∽

I know that young people have a zeal for adventure, but an 80-year-old adrenaline junkie? It comes as a shock, not only for me but for the entire group of people who are a part of this event. My nanny reminds me of a warrior riding a wild horse with a spear in their hand. I wonder where she gets all that energy from.

'We are going river rafting!' my cousin says with excitement, rounding us up in the corridor of The Elgin Silver Oaks in Kalimpong. Mehek and Janvi arrive from the plains to enjoy the adventurous terrain. Our group includes six members of the Oberoi family.

'This is the exact number of people we need. Six members to go on the raft. Grab your change of clothes and especially sunscreen, everyone. The concierge has booked our slot for noon. We have to hurry! It is an hour's drive down the valley. Just a quick reminder before we face the rapids,' Mehek says, grabbing her little sister by the waist.

'Kamla Didi, please ask Mehek to stop bothering me,' little Janvi says, gazing at her own nanny, who's wearing a bright yellow saree. Mountain girls have adventure written all over them and it shows in their lifestyle. From climbing the terrifying Tenzing rock to being a part of the Himalayan Mountaineering Institute and paragliding our way through the valley's highest point, we love all sports. But Kamla Didi knows this is not her calling and takes a step back.

'Kamla, don't be such a scaredy cat. You are young at heart—barely past the age of 67.' Jethi grabs Kamla's saree even though the latter is hiding behind her.

Kamla has been under Jethi's wing right from the start, even though the difference in their height tells another story— Kamla towers over my five-foot-tall nanny, trying to hide her large body. It is a failed attempt through and through.

My 80-year-old nanny is not included in this rafting adventure for obvious reasons, but that is not going to stop her from being a part of it. Jethi already has a change of clothes in the suitcase that she packed for us. None of us question Jethi's presence as she accompanies us everywhere we go. But not in my wildest dreams could I have imagined that an 80-year-old lady would enjoy river rafting.

'I am taking the front seat. I have been looking forward to this all day.' Jethi says, tightening up her and our life jackets. The instructor too seems like a little rabbit as he sits facing the oncoming rapids beside Jethi.

Jethi is no ordinary person; she seems to be enjoying the process as she wipes river water off her face and glasses. Believe it or not but the first person to jump on the raft and venture abroad among us all was my nanny. Not only did she travel abroad but she also lived in Scotland. She worked with a British family, staying on their farm, for over ten years. She was professionally trained by them to be attentive to even the smallest detail with respect to housekeeping and governing their large estate. Jethi is a force of nature. She is an excellent governess; she helped bring up five children while in Scotland, a tradition she continued while raising us three siblings here in India. Viraj, Aanyaa and I are the lucky ones. Jethi is a perfectionist to the core. No fork could be placed on the wrong side of the plate nor will there be the smallest stain on your table napkin under her watch. She has the eyes of a hawk. I suspect another two are behind her head as well because nothing goes unnoticed while she is in the vicinity. From the Scottish Isles to a hotel named after a town in Scotland, Jethi's destiny is aligned with our lives. And it doesn't stop there. She is also a citizen of the United Kingdom. She never ceases to flaunt it either, especially when some guests in the hotel undermine her, assuming she would not understand the English language due to her Tibetan features. Once, standing straight, very politely, she answered their questions in perfect English, astonishing the guests. In her sweet Tibetan accent, Jethi said, 'While I love India, I do have some cherished memories of my time in the UK. It has been my home for many years when I was a young woman in my thirties.' Jethi then engaged the guests with her tales of travel while seated at the cosy gazebo, overlooking the serene Himalayas. She captures their attention to such an extent that many especially ask after her and welcome her presence and a conversation with her each time they visit. A guest from Denmark once remarked, 'She has the soul of a true mountaineer. Her stories take people into the deep valleys of the Himalayas.'

Making her presence felt like a sturdy rock, Jethi says, 'I am part of the Sherpa community of mountaineers and my earlier life was at a small village in Nepal, near the foothills of Mount Everest. My father and brother were regular climbers and I knew the land like the back of my hand. My simple life as a young mountain girl changed when dark clouds overshadowed my childhood. I was an innocent teenager who transformed overnight into a responsible woman with the stroke of fate's lightning. My brother met with a tragic end while climbing the unforgiving Mount Everest. Hit by an avalanche, he could not survive the wrath of snow. His loss was the beginning of my suffering. My father fell ill soon after. Consumed by grief, the chilly mountains snatched his soul into their icy embrace. I felt the glaciers crashing over me as both the men in my life were taken by the mountains. Leaving that life behind, I turned towards a new land and made Darjeeling my home. The land of the thunderbolt has been very kind to me. It is my land of solace and security. Life has thrown many daggers at me, but I have learned to survive its harshness. After all, my hair hasn't turned grey just by chance.'

'Living here at The Elgin with all of you is a second life granted to me by God. I am blessed to have more than one family in one lifetime. Many people don't even get the happiness of one. Must be my karma. I am linked to you in this birth as closely as a river is to the ocean,' Jethi continues. She captures the attention of visitors from all around the globe, turning the mood into anything but grey. Living up to her soul's mission of being someone who lights up everyone's lives, she also spreads courage and endurance. This spiritual nanny of mine is certainly an extraordinary one. Her face bears wrinkles of sadness, yet her eyes are full of joy.

∽

One fine day, I see one of the most astonishing matches of all time taking place under our very own roof. The crowd swells around the stars of the show. News of an arm-wrestling challenge is floating through the halls.

'Who are the contenders?' I wonder. An arena has been set up in the Rhododendron Lounge with a large round table. The general manager and the head governess are seated on opposite sides, ready to take up the challenge. They are certainly going head-to-head.

'Come on! Come on!' The crowd consists of housekeeping staff, butlers, receptionists and even chefs who have come out of the kitchen to witness the challenge, and all of them are cheering the contenders. The cold lounge begins to turn warmer and everyone is enthusiastically placing bets on the match—'500 rupees if the general manager wins…1,000 rupees if it's Jethi…2,000 if the manager wins...'

Jethi rolls up the sleeves of her golden blouse and removes a turquoise ring from her middle finger. Badal, in contrast, takes off his gold cufflinks, accepting the challenge. Both parties show off their strength by flexing their biceps, one after the other. Jethi tightens up the knot of her salt and pepper hair while also tightening up her Tibetan bakhu. At that moment, I know—*hoc est bellum*—this is war! With strong hands, Jethi takes hold of the general manager's palm. The head chef, dressed accordingly with his *toque* in place, is acting as a referee with a red tablecloth in his hand. It feels as if raging bulls are about to be released, with steam blowing out of their nostrils.

'One…two...three!' The match begins. And… 'Boom! Man down!' A loud sound comes from the lounge. Within five seconds, the general manager's wrist is locked down on the table... Absolutely flat.

'How could this happen?' Badal is shocked by his shameful defeat. His face turns flaming red with embarrassment. He is defeated in front of his entire cavalry. The crowd is cheering in the Rhododendron Lounge, brimming with laughter, while Jethi fixes her glasses and gives a proud smile.

'I'm a Sherpa! Let's ride the avalanches, shall we?' she

boasts in a confident tone. Rolling up her sleeves, she is ready for round two. 'Come on, Badal! Are you upset so soon? You look like a cloud that's about to burst into rain. You are most definitely a *ghana badal*, an ominous cloud, in the sky!'

The general manager now has to prove his might to his army. Being the centre of attention in defeat is something he didn't bargain for. In the next round, Badal puts all his concentration in the match and says, 'I let you win, Jethi. I didn't want to put all my strength into it in one go, but this time I will not hold back. I hope you are ready?'

Jethi, accepting the challenge, says, 'Yes, yes! Come on! One more round. I have just warmed up.'

The second the bids reach up to 5,000 rupees, our chef and referee ring the bell for the next round.

With unwavering concentration, both their elbows are locked on the flat wooden table firmly. Both Jethi and Badal are unwilling to let go of their grip, not even an inch is being given away. I watch Jethi's rough hands gripping the general manager's strong palms. Their wrists are locked, with pressure being applied at the optimum angle. A few seconds on the clock and their hands move, inch towards the left, then shift towards the right. A little later their locked wrists are upright again. On the neutral ground. It goes on like this for another two or three minutes, when suddenly, 'Boom!' The general manager's hand is down flat on the table.

'Victory!' Jethi shouts. 'Oh, how I love the sense of power. No better adrenaline rush than beating a young man. I am a woman of steel! I am a Sherpa of true Himalayan blood! I can conquer any mountain!' Jethi believes that women are born with an innate strength that enables them to bear immense physical pain, like that of childbirth. She never lets any opportunity pass her by to prove this point. She is the epitome of self-efficacy. Jethi gathers her prize money, bows down to thank the crowd with folded hands and resumes her role as a governess. The general manager, now defeated, leaves to resume his duty at the front desk.

The words, 'with compliments', vanished from the general manager's vocabulary that particular day. Ever since this arm-wrestling challenge, Jethi has been looked upon with respect and pride by the entire organization. All the women are inspired by her while the men feel intimidated. She's truly a role model for both the young and elderly at The Elgin.

'Age is just a number. I can take down men half my age and double my size if I must.' My 80-year-old nanny's voice rings inside the hotel walls, giving us a mental boost.

5

KARMA

Within the hotel walls, we often forget that we are living alongside more than a hundred people at a time. It surely is a large family. A group of people who have no ties to each other except for their work, yet share a strong social connection. The hotel provides our employees with a sense of belonging and an identity. The Elgin comprises a large number of individuals who come from all walks of life, from different communities, speak varied languages and belong to contrasting cultures. It is something we feel proud of, a place that unites us all.

We have been brought together either by choice or chance. I believe that it may be destiny playing a part in our lives, placing us here together at this very moment in time, thereby making our bond priceless. *Is this our karma? One can only wonder in the land of the Buddha.*

On one freezing February day, I lay thinking about destiny and how some things feel like they're meant to be. *Does the universe conspire to put people in a set location in the fabric of time that has no rational explanation?* This thought keeps running through my mind. My eyes fall on my mother, sitting on the lush grass of the lawn. She loves to feel the soft grass under her bare feet, saying it keeps her grounded and makes her feel closer to Mother Earth. *It is a simple yet deep-rooted idea*, I think, and I am inspired to follow her, quite literally.

Parents are the child's first and best teachers, after all; they teach us to take our first steps and utter our first words, and we learn everything we know—whether it be to survive or build our individual character—from them.

'Come here, Rea!' my mother shouts. She is wearing her glamorous cat-eye sunglasses under the glaring winter sun. 'Come, my dear, have some fresh oranges. This batch is absolutely delicious and has a really sweet taste. You will relish it as your taste buds match mine. I especially had them picked from our orange tree below. Remember the one Badi Mama, your grandmother, planted herself? The fruits have turned out so sweet. And what a lovely sunny day it is! I want to sit outside for a while and enjoy the weather before the clouds glide in,' she says with a joyous smile stretching all the way to her blushing cheeks.

I quickly head to the garden, take off my knee-high leather boots to sit right next to her and eat the oranges that she is peeling. Peter and Lilian rush towards us from their kennel and pounce one after the other on my mother. Suddenly, the string of her pink rose quartz bracelet breaks and the beads scatter over the grass.

'Not again! I just cannot wear jewellery any more with you two going straight for it.' My mother gathers herself, then suddenly she pauses and says, 'How strange, Rea, all of a sudden, I remember an old incident.'

I, too, grow inquisitive. 'What is it, Mama? Which incident? I hope it is a happy one,' I say, relishing the sweet taste of the home-grown oranges.

'It is something I was thinking about sitting here on the grass. An incident that happened years ago, around the time when you were born.'

'Is it about me? Go on, tell me,' I say excitedly.

'Okay, so listen carefully. It's a story of a karmic connection! Whatever you put into the universe you get right back. Einstein's theory of relativity is similar. Every action has an equal and opposite reaction. I have experienced this universal law first-hand. A zone where science and spirituality converge; they intertwine like two branches of a flowering tree. When I was pregnant with you, I was in urgent need of a blood donor because you were born by caesarean, which led to heavy blood loss. As fate had it, my blood group is O+. While we can donate to anyone with a positive blood group, it's not quite the same the other way around because as a recipient we're compatible with either the O+ or O– blood type only. Your father's blood group is B+, and so is yours, Aanyaa's and Viraj's. All three children somehow took after their father. While on the hunt for the matching blood type, with your Papa frantically searching for a donor in the entire hotel, he surprisingly found one person who was capable of doing it. Guess who? This person is our head chef, Mr Padam. He willingly accompanied Diamond to the hospital. He sat there in a very calm and composed manner and gave me his blood. I was shocked to see Mr Padam in my half-unconscious state. "Diamond Sir, I am petrified of needles and hospitals but I will do this for Nimmi memsahib," Mr Padam said out loud. He closed his eyes tight and began his breathing exercises to calm his nerves. I was overcome with emotion at his selfless gesture and could not thank him enough. He touched my heart with his kindness at a moment when I needed it the most.'

I am surprised by this information. I meet the chef almost every day in the hotel premises, all without knowing this fact that connects him to me personally. This is literally an indirect blood bond. As soon as I have this thought, my mother continues, 'Wait a minute, Rea! The story doesn't end here. Years passed by, leading me to this one particular day when I was at the reception engrossed in a conversation with the hotel's guests. Suddenly, the front desk manager came rushing towards me with an emergency. I politely excused myself from the conversation and went towards the kitchen, following the manager with haste. To my surprise, I saw Head Chef Padam lying on the floor, unconscious. We rushed towards him to pull him up on the bench. The hotel doctor was immediately called, but his situation was getting worse by the minute so we quickly took him to the nearby hospital. The doctors confirmed that earlier this week he had undergone an appendix operation, which had resulted in excessive loss of blood. He needed a blood donor at the earliest. At that very moment we all knew who that donor was going to be. I heard a sudden voice calling out to me from within. It felt as though it was meant to be. My presence, at that very instant, was not an accident. It was a calling, saying that I needed to clear my karmic debt. It felt like the universe was smiling at us saying, see how beautiful the world is, how connected we all are without even realizing it. We are all branches of the tree of life. We affect each other's world in surprising ways. We are placed together in this fabric of time for a higher purpose. Nothing on earth occurs just by chance, Rea. It is my karma. *Astra inclinant, sed non obligant*; the stars incline us, they do not bind us.'

My sweet mother's words send me to the realm of karma when, in the distance, I see Aanyaa walking through the gates of The Elgin with the whole gang. Looks like the family is back from their walk, one which my mother and I slyly escaped.

'Hello there,' shouts Aanyaa, waving her hands at us. I see Jethi, Papa and Dorjee, the driver, following behind her like a straight line of ants, one after the other, carrying goodies.

'What are my lovely ladies doing?' asks my father, grabbing a spot on the grass next to us.

Aanyaa goes straight for the Darjeeling oranges and says, 'Spill the beans on what you were talking about.' She turns to my mother while relishing the oranges.

'Well, Aanyaa, you have caught us at the right time. We are in the middle of discussing your favourite topic. Karma!' my mother says, placing her hand on my sister's head, gently blessing her. A gesture of love in our land.

'You ladies have ventured into the land of karma, I see!' Aanyaa is ready to explore the topic when we hear Jethi, who is seated next to her, speak. 'Being a Buddhist, I cannot deny this. Buddhism strongly believes in the concept of karma. I feel it is something that truly affects our life in this lifetime or the next.'

We are drawn towards Jethi's spiritual self. 'What do you mean by that, Jethi? Do you feel we will have a next life? A rebirth?' Aanyaa seeks to know more.

'Yes, I believe so, Aanyaa. We fulfil our karma with actions in this life itself, till we carry forward the remaining karma onto our next life. Our rebirth. We reap what we sow in one way or another. Just as the earth is round, everything comes right around.'

Aanyaa is lost in cosmic configuration and agrees with her wise words. 'Hmm. You may be on to something there, Jethi. Our wise owl that you are. The concept of karma may be possible as it is evident in the very movement of our universe. Right from the rotation and revolution of our planets to the shape of this round orange in my hand. I can understand where you are coming from, Jethi.' Aanyaa begins to think deeply about this topic.

Being a seeker of deep knowledge and science, Aanyaa leans

towards her spiritual self. Jethi holds her cold hands in her own and says, 'You know, Aanyaa, maybe our present birth is a culmination of our past karma. I am born in this form and have been through a rollercoaster of a life maybe because of my past. My karma. In this life, I have faced many hardships and did not have the privilege of being born with a silver spoon in my mouth. My appearance is not that of a swan either. The only thing I aspire for is to achieve my final goal of nirvana. If not, I pray to have a better next birth. You never know I may come back in this house as your son. Next time, I may be reborn as a man. A dashing, rich man. In absolute contrast to this life of mine. If I take rebirth in this house, then you three children will do what I did for you growing up. You will have to take care of me, feed me and bathe me. Then it will be time to fulfil your karma with me!' Jethi gives Aanyaa the most meaningful hug, her eyes turning dewy and full of compassion. Under the February sun, I watch my governess and my elder sister share a profound observation of the universe through each other's perspective.

6

MY BUTLER, THE FOREST SHAMAN

The private butler at The Elgin is as extraordinary as the rest of the hotel. The Elgin and Mr Butler can receive the same status of being 'heritage'. Both of them are cut from the same cloth; they're both wise and have withstood time. To have one without the other leaves an incomplete painting on our Himalayan canvas.

I walk into the cosy Elgin Bar to see a five-foot-six-inch man standing up straight in his customized uniform of white and gold, which includes a traditional white turban and a shiny gold-plated badge engraved with his name Mr Butler. It is polished by him every day as soon as he starts his work day. Also, Mr Butler doesn't come alone. His wife Malini works as a gardener in the hotel. This couple has been a part of the hotel for more than three decades and has helped my grandfather transform the old cottage of Elgin when he initially purchased it from the Maharaja of Cooch Behar. Butler and Malini make a dynamic duo and have seen Elgin right from when its foundation bricks were being laid. During the British Raj, Elgin Cottage was sublet and run under the management of Nancy Oakley. She came to India from Scotland and named the summer house of the Maharaja after her home town, Elgin. Mr Butler and his wife have been a constant presence, adding to the charm, heritage, warmth and persona of the hotel. Some of our guests enjoy Mr Butler's cheerful presence and repeatedly ask for his service during their multiple visits. They get overjoyed upon seeing a familiar face greeting them on their Himalayan vacation.

His real name is still a secret for many of us as he insists on being addressed only as Mr Butler. He feels a sense of pride in that name. It is his identity now. Mr Butler and Malini are our oldest employees, and most definitely the wisest ones. As you get to know Mr Butler and engage in a conversation with him, you will find there is much more to him than what initially meets the eye. A hidden personality lurks behind that polished outward attire. He plays more than one role in our life. While twirling his perfectly shaped moustache, Mr Butler has a light in his eyes unlike that in any ordinary man. He has a speciality in working with the 'Chi' element. The hidden avatar of Mr Butler is that of a healer, what the local dwellers of the mountains call a 'witch doctor' or a *banjhakri*, a forest shaman. Mr Butler belongs to the original inhabitants of Darjeeling, known as the Lepchas. He works with energy and natural elements and is well-versed in ancient enchantments that ward away evil spirits, thereby bringing a supernatural element into our lives.

I watch him collecting some herbs from the Duchess Garden, singing slowly while he picks them. 'Good afternoon, Mr Butler. What magic potion are you brewing today? I see you are collecting ingredients with such undivided attention,' I say while standing under a white garden umbrella.

Mr Butler does not answer at first, and he continues singing till he completes his ritual. 'Good afternoon, Rea. I see you have come to spy on my secret ingredients.'

I watch him turn towards me under the strong rays of the mountain sun. Suddenly, a ray of light reflects off his neck where lies an aquamarine stone on a thick silver chain, shaped like a teardrop. The quality of the gem is unmatched and so is its significance. It is secretly known as 'the shaman's stone'. With a smiling face and almond eyes, Mr Butler says, 'Rea, this aquamarine gem has special powers that help us shamans meditate and communicate with the higher realms. We call it astral walking. It works as a tool to help our vision, and our foresight becomes much clearer. Aquamarine's crystalline nature works wonders for various healing purposes in our rituals. My gem is energized with Kanchenjunga's blessings, the Lepchas' sacred mountain. I kept the aquamarine submerged in three different Himalayan rivers for three months to harness its energy inside the gem. Once my ritual was complete, I wore it around my neck, close to my heart.'

Mr Butler has profound knowledge of the surrounding forest and of the curing abilities of nature, which he uses to heal the sick across the land. The Lepchas of the Himalayan mountains have an ancient tradition passed down by forest shamans, *banjhakris*, who remove imbalances of energy or evil entities wandering in the forests and heal the sick. Shamans are not just legends in our hill station. They live among us, as a part of our society. As I venture deep into the remote Lepcha villages of Darjeeling, their culture connects me with their ancient roots. The forest shamans live in no secrecy. Some have lived in that exact spot or that same village for decades under the shadow of their sacred mountain—the Kanchenjunga. The mystical mountains have shamans and energy healers as their light workers and spiritual healers. They have miraculously kept their secret traditions alive, even in the twenty-first century. People living here maintain their equilibrium with nature. Shamans, especially, have a connection with the unknown forests. Unless the natural elements are tampered with, the forest shamans are not summoned.

One night last September, a local villager complained to the head priest about energy fluctuations in his house, leading to an eerie feeling within the premises. The lights in his room were flickering in the dark. His doors and windows opened and closed of their own accord, frightening him. His young nephew fell sick immediately after these strange occurrences with no signs of a physical ailment. He seemed to have been affected by some unknown negative energy in the forest. The young man had constant nightmares and developed a fear of coming in contact with people; he was stuck in his house for days. The head priest of the temple called for Mr Butler to heal the young man. Mr Butler is a revered forest shaman in the town and is known for his wisdom. He's always willing to perform his spiritual duty and so, he went to this man's house with a handful of special herbs he had picked from the adjoining forest. He performed his ceremony of removing the 'evil eye' from the young boy. Holding a traditional circular drum made of animal skin, Mr Butler began to chant his mantras. Holding three trumpet lilies in his hand, he sang songs of his ancestors. He asked the boy to rest and instructed his uncle to report back to him the next day about the progress in the young boy's health. The next morning, as Mr Butler was on his daily duty in the hotel, a messenger arrived, laden with fruits and a 'thank you' note for Mr Butler; the boy had shown signs of recovery.

Himalayan people hold the forest shamans in high regard because their healing abilities have a profound effect on the various ailments of the mind and body. A forest shaman's knowledge of energy distribution, the earth's biological properties and celestial movements is useful for its people's welfare. They are our physicians, psychiatrists and spiritual guides. A forest shaman's secret knowledge is passed down verbally, from master to student, transforming the student into a master. It may appear strange to us but it is priceless and limitless.

Mr Butler clears his throat and says, 'Shamans have the ability to connect to the spirit realm. This hidden knowledge is orated through songs, tales and practical rituals, designed to connect the earth's grid to our very own. *Banjhakris* act as a medium between unlimited cosmic energy and the body as a vessel. Shamans can communicate with spirits to pass information to their families here on earth. If a person dies a sudden, unnatural death, shamans help the family get closure by asking the deceased their final wishes. We call this ritual *chinta*. I attained this knowledge from an elderly shaman in a cave. I remember the moment my guru opened up the doors to astral walking. Dark cold water was dripping from the mouth of the cave, which possessed an unusual silence.'

Mr Butler whispers the story into the wind. I take a walk with the forest shaman into his natural habitat for a mystical Himalayan rendezvous.

7

THE LEPCHAS AND THEIR ORIGINS

Darjeeling's first local inhabitants are the Lepcha or Rong, who call this land their home. Within The Elgin's diverse walls, we have members from this community working with us for decades. The depth of their culture is as old as the land itself. Various folklore surrounding this community takes a deep dive into their mythology, culture and tradition. I have a special place in my heart for the Lepchas as I have grown up with one of them. Mr Butler is Lepcha and is well known for his other powerful profession—a forest shaman, witch doctor or *banjhakri*, as the locals call it. Mr Butler has shared some of his sacred knowledge with me; the Himalayan legends and life lessons that he imparted to me have helped shape my 'light bearer' personality. His deep voice still echoes like music in my mind; his teachings are imprinted on us all at The Elgin. Mr Butler became an integral part of the family through the years, while his tales became a habit, a way to disconnect from the world and enter the Lepchas' pathways. Mr Butler, being an eloquent orator, is my teacher, spiritual master and guide, who helps me live life to the fullest.

Mr Butler gently places a camellia sapling on the soil and covers it up with wet earth. He says, 'Lepchas transfer their sacred knowledge through storytelling and songs passed down the bloodline. It is my duty to keep our traditions alive or it will be lost in the deep vacuum of time and space.' His teachings include ancient legends and traditional rituals that shed light upon a hidden culture.

I hold the wet earth in my hand and say, 'Knowledge passed down through generations among the Lepchas is now my responsibility as well. I feel as though I am a part of the Lepchas, Mr Butler. Don't you agree? I have an understanding of its roots, beliefs and values thanks to you. I wonder which level of understanding I am on.'

Mr Butler brightens up our mornings with his radiant smile and expressive button eyes. Round spectacles sit on the bridge of his compact nose, while his moustache is curled to perfection. He is at his usual spot, standing alert at the Duke Hall, busy with his chores. I walk in to find him alone in the busy morning hours. How strange! The grandfather clock tells us the time—it's 8 a.m. and not even a bird is around. Mr Butler is polishing the silver vigorously, rubbing every inch of the forks.

'Good morning, Mr. Butler. How is our shaman today?' I say, pulling up a chair to the round breakfast table. 'What shall I have for breakfast today? How about some baked beans on toast, a sunny side up and some Lepcha legends for dessert,' I say with a wink.

Mr Butler continues to polish the silver. He begins to hum a strange chant. He pauses for a moment to dig deep into his memories. 'Tales of the Lepchas begin with the beginning of time itself. As the world was formed by the Almighty, the Lepchas were created as the first two human beings, male and female, from whom the population of the entire planet has descended. The Lepchas were created by God Aitbu Deburoom from the fresh fallen snow of the mighty Kanchenjunga range. He called the first man, Fudongthing, and the first woman, Nazong Nyu. This is the reason why the

Lepchas call themselves the "children of the snowy peak". The story of creation and mankind begins here. My grandmother hummed a song to me when I was a child. She sang the song of creation.' The shaman whispers with a strong and steady voice. His hazel eyes glitter in the sunlight as he tells the tale of the Lepchas and their first people.

'The roots of our people are hidden somewhere in these Himalayas. This mountain range is sacred to our people because our origins can be traced to this mountain itself. Our motherland is known as "the land of eternal purity". The Lepchas live in the foothills of the Kanchenjunga and are blessed with a spectacular view of this holy range. Can I tell you a secret, Rea? There is a hidden village among these foothills whose location is only known to the elderly Lepchas, and it is strictly passed down through their bloodline. It is believed that every Lepcha must go to this village before their death and conduct rituals sacred to the Kanchenjunga to pass over to the other side. This tradition is conducted even today. The Lepchas hold ancient knowledge of the land and secrets of the afterlife within their community. These tales have been passed down to me by my grandfather and his grandfather before him. This information has deep sentimental value, which I feel I could share with you today.' Mr Butler calmly gazes at me and I instantly feel a tingle in my bones.

He says, 'Ancient Lepcha legends sing the song of a young man. A man who treaded for days and days without exhaustion taking hold of him. A young Lepcha man was hunting deep in these forests when something caught his attention in the stream. A strange piece of wood came floating towards him— something not from this forest. It had blue needles instead of regular leaves and the bark glimmered like gold. The young man let his inquisitive nature take it as a sign from his Gods.

The young Lepcha began to walk uphill to find the source of the floating bark. The tree had to be somewhere in the high mountains. He walked for days and nights, crossing dense forests and snow-clad mountains and discovered a quaint valley, with a serene lake filled with white feathered birds he had never seen before. These white birds covered the lake with a blanket of white feathers. He continued on his journey to reach a large emerald-green valley surrounded by peaks of snow. He instantly knew in his heart that he had entered the home of his ancestors—the hidden valley of Mayel. He stumbled upon a little hut with the cold moon almost upon him. It was beginning to get dark. He decided to take shelter for the night. An old Lepcha woman opened the door and offered him milk, grain and fruits. She brought with her hot water and a rug for the young visitor. She was joined by an old man who lived with her. The couple stayed here in peace and solace. The young Lepcha fell asleep after a long journey and woke to something surprising. He saw two children playing in the courtyard. Their carefree sounds lightened the young Lepcha's heart. He wondered where the old couple was. There were no adults in sight. Not one! How strange. He went to interact with the children and came to know something that shook the ground under his feet. The children giggled at the young Lepcha and said, "Hello there, I hope you have had a good night's rest. Didn't you recognize us? We are the old couple. Don't be startled. Our world is designed this way. As the sun rises, we shapeshift into children during the morning, adults in the day, and old age in the evening. This cycle continues the next day. A constant shift in our physical form. It is how we remain immortal. Our secret to everlasting life. You can stay here at Mayel for a period of seven days and nights, then you must return to your village. Mortals are meant to keep away from Mayel. I wonder how a young man like you came into our hidden valley. It is a calling from this sacred space. Take these seeds of grain with you. It will solve the problem of hunger for your people."

'The young Lepcha lived for seven days and nights in the magical valley till he had to return to his village. On the seventh night, before leaving, he asked the old lady for instructions about how to sow the seeds. The old lady said, "You must sow the seeds at the right time. That is the trick for a good harvest." As the old lady uttered those words, a flock of magnificent white birds flew past them, turning the dark sky white with their feathers. The old lady let the land guide her and said, "This will be the signal to sow the seeds. A flock of white birds will fly through the sky. You will know the right time has come." The young Lepcha left the land of his ancestors with the treasure and happy tears.'

I will carry with me Mr Butler's wisdom for the future generations of my own family. This gesture of acceptance truly touched my heart. The Lepcha shaman considered us family and made sure we knew it. He introduced me to his world of the *banjhakris*.

Darjeeling has an ancient culture and Mr Butler is a revered part of the shaman community of learned men, who are also known as the 'wise ones'. One winter night, Mr Butler sat me down with a cup of green tea and began to shed light on the story of his life. He began to uncover the ideology of the Himalayan shamans and how he ended up becoming one. He opened a window into his life and said, 'I was taught the ancient arts by an elderly shaman who chose me at a very young age to carry this ancient tradition to the next generation.' He went on and said, 'If you asked the elders in the community, they would tell you that some young boys disappeared from their villages and suddenly reappeared after a few years from the dense forest.'

Mr Butler lowered his tone and deepened his voice to say, 'These young boys were taken into the forest by the *banjhakri* for a couple of years till they learned the rituals and became apprentices of the forest shaman. These boys were taught the magic of the land and the healing properties of the wild vegetation, along with secret spells and medicinal herbs to heal the sick. I was taken into the forest at the age of seven to become an apprentice of one of the forest shamans who needed to impart this knowledge before his death so that the tradition of the *banjhakri* was not lost forever. I lived with my teacher for 10–12 years. I was sent back when I was ready to become a forest shaman myself. This moment in my life is what transformed me into a *banjhakri*.'

Mr Butler's ability to ward off evil spirits and sickness from the villagers has made him a revered man among his people. He is well respected in his community, and they see him as a healer. Ever since I was a child I have seen Mr Butler's healing abilities. On occasions, when my family felt under the weather, Mr Butler would come up to the room with a small black hat filled with tiny trumpet flowers. While we sat on the couch, our shaman towered above us in the silent room and began his ritual by singing spells in his language, with the trumpet flowers lying in the centre of his hat. He then gently moved the flowers around our heads multiple times before placing them back inside the hat and said, 'This is an ancient technique of removing *nazar* or the evil eye.' Our shaman prayed for a couple of minutes and asked us to drop a coin into the black hat. With his eyes closed, he said, 'This is a means of energy exchange. By giving me a copper coin you have concluded our exchange while balancing our energies.' This ritual was usually performed when we were severely sick—either with a fever or a cold. Mr Butler then explained, 'Madam, it is an age-old tradition of cleansing ourselves and removing any negative energy that has come into our auric field, which in turn affects our general health. As you walk around the open mountains there is a possibility that one may pick up some unwanted energies from the unknown forest, especially during dusk when the veil between the worlds is thin. There are different forms of energy scattered in our surroundings, and sometimes one can unknowingly pick it up. These flowers and sacred mantras are a way to remove it from the physical body. This is a cleansing ritual we shamans perform. The unknown forest is home to many energy spectrums—positive and negative—and it is my duty to give you a heads up.'

Mr Butler's way of life leaves us all wondering for days, questioning the true meaning of life. He speaks only about energy. I don't recall a moment when he used the words 'good' or 'bad'. The shaman solely concentrates on the positive and negative. Mr Butler says, 'Good and bad are strong terms in nature. Wild animals hunt and kill only to sustain themselves. That is the way of nature. This does not make animals evil. It is their basic instinct of survival. In contrast, mankind brings greed, ambition and power into play. In the natural world, cosmic energy relies on balance. This is the key. If you successfully balance your energies, then you can achieve blissful peace in this world.'

What a beautiful state of mind, where everything exists in balance, dancing to the tunes of harmony, resembling the day and night, sun and moon. Two contrasting energies are needed to create balance.

'Can we live in perpetual daylight without night? Or can we live in perpetual darkness without the sun? It is not possible.

Life has these contrasting aspects that are equally important for existence. Is darkness bad? At night, we get to heal our bodies. Deep sleep removes all signs of stress and toxicity and helps us to embrace the next day,' says the shaman.

I admire the way Mr Butler shares his learnings with us. I eagerly await for when I will next hear something yet unheard of from Mr Butler.

He continues, 'Rea, let me shed light on the concept of the soul. Remember that one should respect everything around us. Every living thing, such as a tree, plant and animal, has a soul. Just because something is out of our understanding does not mean it does not exist. Our planet has a consciousness that is alive. Once we begin to look at our planet with empathy, we start caring for it rather than destroying it. Forest shamans take from nature only what is needed, nothing more. As humans, we are taught that our wants are unlimited, but in reality, we have to respect our planet and curb our wants. Take only what is necessary while letting nature run its course. Our planet provides us with abundant resources but once we bend towards destroying the balance of nature to satiate our greed and desires, Mother Nature will not be able to sustain us anymore. We need to draw a line between our needs and our desires. This is simply what defines a good human being.'

Mr Butler's wise words have shaped the way Aanyaa and I look at the planet. Our ability to live in harmony with nature makes us the people we are today.

8

GYPSIES IN CARAVANS

The month of May is marked by the shimmering sun and clear skies, with cumulus clouds moving swiftly through the valley. Rainbows are our regular visitors, yet there is something very unusual in the air on this particular day. The sparrows arrive in the morning with a surprise. I spot a fleet of caravans parked outside in the hotel's driveway. I instantly know that some interesting guests have arrived at The Elgin.

It is 6 a.m. and everything outside is silent, with many not yet awake. I get dressed in a hurry and run down the wooden staircase from my attic to the reception. I put on my explorer hat and noise-cancellation earphones to venture into the realm of the gypsies. I look at the courtyard in wonderment as a group of European travellers arrive in their creative caravans.

I see the bellboys unloading their suitcases; I want to take a quick look inside. I am so curious that I can't help it any longer... Putting the rules aside for a few minutes, I decide to peek inside one of the caravans.

A horseshoe is nailed above the door, a sign of good luck, I presume, enhancing the caravan's rustic charm. I open the door and observe that the caravan has a washroom, a sitting area and a foldable bed at the back. It is divided by a sheer curtain into two parts. I notice a narrow ladder leading to the roof. Quietly, I climb up the ladder in this unusual vehicle and find a space on the roof that consists of a bedroom inside a tent-like structure. A chime is hanging from the tiny window. A white dreamcatcher is swaying in the wind, flaunting its delicate feathers. I am thrilled to see such an exciting automobile. I have been at The Elgin during antique car shows hosted in town, always gazing from a distance, but this one is a first. I am breaking some serious ground rules by treading inside a caravan belonging to the guests who have checked in. But a quick glance wouldn't hurt anyone, would it? *The caravan is unlocked as it is. So I am not breaking and entering, or am I? I wonder who these people are.* I feel adventure coursing through my veins while my mind is brimming with curiosity. I always dream of exploring the world in my very own caravan someday. To venture wherever I want, sleep in the wilderness under the Milky Way, near a river bank or on a mountaintop. My imagination is taking me places. For a second, I want to join the European group on their upcoming adventures. I'm sure they won't mind a plus one. Not pushing my luck any further, I walk back to the hotel and sit by the window in the lobby, observing the guests as they relax on the couch, sipping their welcome drinks. I think it is a bit too early for our customary cherry brandy so a fresh rhododendron juice was their choice of morning nectar.

'Hello there!' I say to the strangers while sipping on my preferred drink—a combination of ginger, turmeric and lemon juice—to give me a head start for the day. Although it is chilly this early in the morning, I get a very friendly hello back. I take the lead in the conversation with the travellers and get to know a newly married couple, Anna and Mathew. The bright red camper van belongs to this young, vibrant and, to my surprise, very normal couple.

They were not the gypsies I imagined them to be, except for their leather jackets and cowboy boots. When I ask, Mathew explains how they embarked on a long journey to explore the Himalayas by road. They lay out their map and show me the ways of an adventurous traveller. Mathew, the entertaining conversationalist, says, 'The path we started on took us to Nepal, and from there we explored the Himalayan kingdom of Bhutan, followed by Sikkim and Northeast India. This is how we ended up here in Darjeeling. My wife and I believe that the only way to feel the true spirit of the land is by doing one thing, and one thing only—grab your suitcase and travel by road. Through quaint villages and Himalayan towns, we feel the spirit of its people. We have been on the road for a month now and have another two months to go before we end our journey.' Anna and Mathew meet different people, familiarize themselves with their many cultures, cross vibrant lakes and moody rivers and encounter exciting wildlife. I can't believe that they lead such an extraordinary life together.

I ask them, 'How long are you planning to stay at The Elgin?' I too want to acquaint myself with them and experience nomadic adventures. At first, I did not disclose my identity and pretended to be another guest at the hotel.

Each following night, I sit by the fire and hear stories of their travels and laugh at the various roadblocks they encounter. I spend days and nights with my thoughts, dreaming and imagining their adventures. One night, I get into bed and I can't sleep as I feel anxious all of a sudden. So I do the one thing I know would fix my mood. I put on my boots and go for a stroll in the Duchess Garden to calm my nerves. Nothing rejuvenates me like some green therapy. I make my way down to the lobby and walk straight towards the parking lot to view these camper vans one more time. I stand outside and look at the vehicles with amusement in the silent night.

I think of taking a better look inside this mechanical marvel because I did not have that much time earlier. I manage to get to the cosy bedroom at the very top using the narrow stairs; the waterproof tent placed there is upright. I am absolutely thrilled to see that I am nearly as high up as the tree branches surrounding The Elgin.

I look at my home and the surroundings in amazement as I have never viewed the hotel from this angle before. Everything looks so different from up here. It is almost an aerial view of The Elgin, like that of an eagle's vision. I spot a bird's nest on the tree branch, clear as day, even during such an odd hour of the night. The moon illuminates my little hamlet. Tree lights enhance the environment, making it possible to see nature up close. I try hopping onto the tree trunk from the corner of the camper van but think of it as a risky move at this time of the night in case I fall. The Elgin looks like a romantic château in the embrace of the lady of the night. I am busy for the next few minutes, imagining a zip line from the camper van's top to my bedroom window. I immediately engineer it in my mind. I am literally on cloud nine as I look around and find myself among the giant treetops of coniferous and oak I have been friends with all my life. Our oldest member of the tree family, called cryptomeria, stands like a stiff and protective guard showing off its physique. Lost in The Elgin's enchantment and the sounds of the forest, I see a shadow moving beneath.

'Who is it?' I ask the moving shadow.

'Neeru? Guard? Guard! Is it you?' I call out from the tent somewhere around the cryptomeria's branches.

'Hello, Rea! It's me, Anna.'

I didn't hear a word. I am lost in my own world. Then, I

see Anna climbing up the narrow stairs. My torchlight reflects the top of her blonde hair, giving away her identity.

'Look who's here! And what are you doing in my house?' Anna teases me as she crawls into the tent.

'Well, Anna. It seems the other way around. Your house is parked inside my house!'

'I am impressed, young lady! Because we are at each other's homes it's time for an age-old nomadic tradition. Let me share a secret with you. Are you ready?' Anna says, grabbing something hidden under the mini-wardrobe in the tent. She stretches her hands, clenched into fists, one by one. 'Rea, choose one. I'll give you ten seconds,' she says, waiting for my answer.

'The right hand,' I say instantly. Anna pauses for a while and opens her left hand instead. She reveals a small box full of thick sticky liquid.

'What is this brown liquid? I do not have a sweet tooth so I am glad of my choice. Is that sugar syrup by any chance?' I ask.

'This is a special kind of honey called mad honey. It is no ordinary honey that you have at your breakfast table. Beware of its sweet veil. Mathew and I ventured deep into a small village in Nepal to discover this unusual honey. It is found specifically in the higher regions of the Himalayas in Nepal. Only a handful of villagers can make the treacherous climb and battle the army of bees. Half a teaspoon of this mad honey can catch someone unawares. When I tasted it for the first time, I experienced a strange light-headed sensation, followed by dizziness and hallucinations. Mathew and I were left stunned by this mysterious honey and kept it as a rare Himalayan find locked in the chest. Let's come down to your choice now. Well, your pick is one with a more graceful demeanour. I must say, good choice, Rea!' she says, finally opening her right hand.

There is a delicate white gypsophila flower.

'I see you have an eye for simplicity and a love for the natural world. Your choice can disclose a great deal about you. This, right here, is the gypsy flower. These tiny flowers are used for cleansing and connecting with Mother Nature, and they hold strong feminine energies within their dainty frame. The white gypsy calls out to you tonight. I would like to gift it to the person it's drawn to. Keep it in your bedroom till the petals turn dry. Then release it into the soil...back to its element.'

As I take the gypsy flower from Anna I can feel its energy flowing through me and I say, 'Thank you for this meaningful gift, Anna. The magic of nature is my true calling. I integrate herbal and natural living in my food, skincare and healing journey. I try to keep it as simple as I can.'

Having a conversation with Anna in her caravan caught us both unravelling ourselves. Anna goes on to say, 'We call the gypsy flower by another name where I am from. It's known as baby's breath there. These pure white beauties symbolize purity, sweetness, innocence and everlasting love. As the name suggests, it is the key to your inner child. These flowers symbolize renewal.'

The baby's breath in my hand is a key to my inner child. *Is it a signal from the cosmos?* I glance towards the dark sky, at Orion's belt. Venus guides me to her shine, giving me a clear sign. Love...

My soul hungers for everlasting love. I wonder. *Who are you? What do you look like?* The stars show me the way and an image of a handsome knight, standing tall, with broad protective shoulders pops in my mind's eye. He is somewhere under the sky. My star mate. *If I am longing for you, are you aching for me too? Come find me wherever you are.* I call out to Venus and my dark knight. *Will we meet in this life?* The gypsy's pink petals call out to me. I blow a delicate petal into the night and wait for my handsome knight to reach me.

9

OUCH! THE THORNY LEAF

Something to watch out for in the northeastern Himalayas is a tiny but terrifying plant called shishnu or the stinging nettle. It is also (infamously) known as the devil's sting. But surprisingly, it is also used by the locals for various purposes, even inculcated into their Himalayan life and diet, and that includes us, members of the Oberoi clan. Shishnu grows freely in these wild mountains and has been a part of the cultural and culinary heritage of the land. It has a notorious reputation in the town, causing a lingering sensation of pleasure and pain through taste and touch, respectively. The chefs may have special recipes for it, but the devil's sting is used by Jethi for not-so-pleasant purposes.

Jethi walks the grounds of The Elgin like a boss, elegantly clad in a vibrant Tibetan bakhu, with her hair neatly put up in a high bun. Her fashion sense is unmatched and the shades of colours she prefers contrast with her moods. Today, my 80-year-old graceful nanny is wearing a reddish hue, which complements her pure white aura. Every evening, as dusk sets in our little town, I know exactly where my governess is; she is usually sitting by the window of Room Number 37 with milky white prayer beads in hand. She chants 'Om Mani Padme Hum' using her family heirloom; the beads are worn out yet still soft. This peaceful avatar of hers emerges only when Aanyaa and I are calmly sitting by the fire, having exhausted all our hyperactive energy.

'Silence your minds to awaken your inner soul.' Jethi is our guru today. 'Today I will teach you to be still. Only then you can look through the clear glass of your soul without ripples. Calm your mind and focus on the sound of the wind. Feel its movement as we tap into the life force of our universe. Our bodies have different chakras of energy, which must keep their constant flow. There are seven prominent wheels in our physical body—starting from our head to our root chakra. The top of the head, where all life begins, is a sensitive spot and is known as the crown chakra, followed by the third eye, throat, heart, solar plexus, sacral and root chakra. Energy flows through them like a tranquil river—smooth and continuous.'

Jethi hums, 'Om Mani Padme Hum', creating ripples in the still room, and says, 'Colours and sounds can help you activate each chakra to align you with the universe. It has been a tool for meditation for centuries. It will connect you to the ultimate source of creation. Close your eyes and think of a colour. It can be any colour that resonates with you first.'

Aanyaa, seated on the floor, replies, 'Blue. This one comes so easily in my vision. Its vibrant light is flashing in my mind.'

Our mortal master replies, 'Now feel that colour pouring into your body, all around this room, seeping through the pores of your skin. Envision blue light piercing through your throat chakra. Keep your focus.'

With our special prayer beads in hand, we imitate her every move. Jethi walks us into the alignment. Our session goes on for an hour in silence and with unwavering concentration. Humming Tibetan Buddhist chants I look towards Aanyaa sitting opposite me and hand over a sketch on paper to break the silence.

'Rea, this is hilarious but accurate. I love it,' my sister

says, bursting into laughter. She instantly takes a pen and lets her wit take over. Aanyaa writes 'Goddess Jethi' in bold letters and hands the paper to our silently praying governess. This distracts her from her meditative state and brings out her more fun side to play. I had drawn a cartoon of Jethi meditating with one eye closed and one open. She is holding a prayer bead in one hand and a deadly stinging nettle leaf in the other.

'Come here, you little brat! Can I get one minute of silence from you two? God forgive me!' She put her prayer beads aside with a sly smile—one we will never forget. A day barely goes by without us getting a good dressing-down from Jethi for obvious reasons.

On one such mischievous day, she raises her Tibetan bakhu to her ankles and runs down the wooden staircase, chasing after us into the garden with the deadly leaf in her hand. It is readily available because it grows naturally in the Himalayas, surrounding our towns and villages. The high altitudes are perfect for its survival but not so much for our survival. I wonder if this is a blessing or a curse for us people from the hills. This deadly natural weapon is called 'the devil's sting' for a very good reason—one sudden strike and your skin will be itching like crazy, with you probably rolling in the hills in anguish because of your burning skin.

My sister and I are the most notorious duo you can come across in this town, full of mischief and pranks. Who said young adults can't have fun? Do we all need to be so serious all the time? We definitely require a strict nanny like Jethi to keep us under control. Or at least try to. Just as the universe knew what to do with us... *Wallah!* Here comes the nanny. Even though she would often give us a good dressing-down, being a strict disciplinarian, Jethi always has a cure for it, with warm cuddles and a hot cup of tea, which she personally makes with bubbles of her love.

'Come here. Sit down and do not jump all over the place,' she says, soon after putting us through such hellfire. She opens up her locked medicine cabinet and reaches for her healing plant, which she keeps in store to relieve us of the agony of the deadly sting. Jethi then begins rubbing the flat dock leaf—the remedy—on the affected area, and suddenly the pain vanishes. 'Girls, I am showing you what love can do. If nature can cause pain, it always has a remedy to cure it too. This is the balance created by the natural world. Don't worry, Jethi has the magical cure ready at all times. I wish you both were a little more ladylike and did not cause such havoc in the hotel; I would not need to resort to this deadly shishnu to get you both under control. It seems like you only hear what I have to say when I have the devil's sting in my hand to frighten you. And yet you two continue to giggle and cause the same havoc the very next day. Look at you both now—already laughing at me. What do I do with you mischievous elves!' she says, pacing up and down, holding her head in dissatisfaction. The words *amor vincit omnia*—love conquers all—are apt for our current situation. Love conquers even the agonizing pricks of the deadly devil's sting. We immediately let out a sigh of relief on being rescued from the stinging hellfire and burst into peals of laughter while Jethi envelopes us in her warm embrace in the aftermath of all the mischief we have caused. Jethi shapes our lives just like a carpenter intricately carves their woodwork. She knows exactly what to say to make our hearts overflow with love. And our hearts have been flowing with love ever since.

10

HOTEL SECRETS

A heritage hotel is incomplete without secret doorways. The large conference hall of The Elgin has a door that leads to a mysterious section of the library, which contains old manuscripts and antiquities that are priceless. The collection varies from ancient historical texts on the great monarchs of England to texts on various cultures from around the world. One of my personal favourites is an antique masterpiece.

I turn the rose gold knob to open the vault and cannot take my eyes off an oil painting of Queen Elizabeth I of England. Her emotive eyes are brimming with life. It's almost like I can feel her pleasure and pain.

She is one of the greatest Tudor monarchs of all time. The unknown artist has captured her on canvas with intricate detail. I am captivated by its magnificence. It is almost lifelike; it feels like she is reaching out from the canvas. I sit on the large window sill with a blank sheet of paper and a pencil in hand. It is a place that inspires me to be true to myself. *Are we not made of love? Are we built to be shoved? Did we begin just to end? Or did we end to begin again?* I pen down my thoughts and write my initials.

Within The Elgin's secret walls lies a priceless handwritten manuscript by Rabindranath Tagore. The Darjeeling hills have been a favourite spot for Tagore to compose his literary gems. We have a deep-rooted connection to Tagore, and his energy and memory still live on in the Himalayas.

I walk across the room of wonder containing countless books left by the previous British owner, Ms Nancy Oakley. She surely had an eye for good things. This room has a magnetic aura. I close my eyes and let my sixth sense guide me. My boots tap on the oak floor as I slowly move westwards. I am drawn towards a chest made of ancient Burma teak. A thought crawls into my mind as soon as I touch its smooth surface. *Artists back in time put in such precise detail and effort into their work. It is evident in their craftsmanship.*

On opening the chest, my eyes stumble upon lithographs by Mr Douglas, the renowned artist. His hand seems to be blessed by a higher power, enabling him to capture life in art form. The sketch looks so lifelike; I am amazed. I gaze into the innocent eyes of a child brought alive in charcoal. The sketch of a little mountain girl in her village takes me into her world. Moving away from the chest, I chance upon another one of our masterpieces—an intricately carved wooden cupboard with an oil painting of a young lady, dating back to a hundred years.

The room of antiquities also contains Himalayan wonders brought back by brave mountaineers who climbed Mount Everest. Something attracts me towards a corner of the secret room. I make my way towards a cabinet I didn't notice before. *A secret within a secret! This looks interesting.* I notice a large uneven rock with a small light illuminating it. This unique piece of rock was brought back to Darjeeling from the summit of Mount Everest. It is a part of our wondrous collection that has been at The Elgin ever since we took over. *What a rare beauty this is. What must it feel like to reach the peak of Everest? It must be mind-blowing.*

Lying next to the rock, on a little satin pillow, is a key.

Next to it is a wooden box. *I have absolutely no idea what the key will unlock...a discovery yet to be made.*

∽

My father has placed an old manuscript on the top rack of the wooden shelf, waiting to be picked up by one of us siblings. Once, while unlocking the door to the room of secrets, my father whispered to me in a serious tone, 'My darling, always remember that knowledge is the key to inner wisdom. The most intriguing piece of knowledge in my collection, and for seekers looking beyond our world, is an ancient book called *The Tibetan Book of Living and Dying* by Sogyal Rinpoche. If you ever feel lonely, my dear, this secret room will keep you company. Here you can spend time fruitfully, and discover something extraordinary to fuel your young mind. Our archives, which contain mysterious antiquities, are a delightful playground for a curious person like you.'

I gaze into the distance to see a rugged thanka on the wall depicting Lord Avalokiteśvara (a bodhisattva who contains the compassion of all Buddhas). He is holding something in his hands, a wish-fulfilling jewel called cintamani. The cintamani is our version of the philosopher's stone and is considered an integral part of Hindu and Buddhist teachings. It has the ability to prolong life and heal the sick. In Buddhism, the cintamani is said to have fallen from the sky in the realm of King Lha Thothori, deep within Tibet. It is one of the four relics that came down from the heavens.

Another piece of antiquity that graces The Elgin is a statue of Gautama Buddha carved out of a single natural mineral. 'My dear, observation is key. These carvings on the mineral, done by an unknown artist, are charming and make it a rare find, even for the greatest of antique collectors.' I recall my father's words from one of our lessons, as our journey takes us from spirituality to mythology and history. My vision moves towards a statue of a lady. This mysterious lady in black wears a jade necklace that dates back hundreds of years. It is one of my favourite pieces among the collectables.

I wonder who this lady is. What a beautiful sculpture. To my surprise, the words 'Mrs Shanti Devi Oberoi' jump out. *My beautiful grandmother. I had a feeling in my bones that I knew this mysterious lady. This must be my grandmother's necklace. How dazzling it looks. I feel a strange connection to it, as though I am time travelling.* I pick up the jade necklace and try it on.

I wonder if I look like her. Maybe just a little bit. I feel her energy around me. I wonder if she is looking down at me from heaven. I feel as though my soul is within my grandmother's embrace, and she's enveloping me in her love. I move towards the centre of the room while wearing the jade necklace. I don't want to take it off. It looks stunning and is comforting at the same time. I spot a glass table with an ornate drawer. I am curious to know its contents. *Letters?* A bunch of envelopes are neatly tucked away. *Hmm... What secrets do you hold?* I pick one up; it is a handwritten letter by the famous author, Dominique Lapierre, stating 'freedom at midnight', addressed to Violet Smith. It is kept as a memory in our archives. It is a special addition to our heritage hotel and is about India's declaration of freedom from the British Raj.

On the left side of the drawer is a peculiar book with torn ends and a dusty surface. I open it to discover that it is an ancient prayer book left behind by a Tibetan monk before he embarked on a pilgrimage from Tibet to Sikkim, making his way towards Darjeeling. His journey is contained in this manuscript and is still preserved in secrecy within these walls. I flip its pages to uncover an ancient map of the land.

I then slowly move into the mystic section of the room, which I call my shanti corner. Another piece of rock (this one brought down from one of the highest lakes on the planet, located on the Tibetan Plateau) is kept in a glass box on display near the window. This rugged rock is from the sacred Gurudongmar Lake, which is among our most prized possessions. Its molecular structure and the religious beliefs surrounding it make this rock unique. Many yogis and saints have gained enlightenment in these majestic Himalayas. Their supernatural abilities of healing with energy and plants that are native to these high altitudes are explained in an old and mysterious manuscript present in our archives.

Next, a piece of parchment kept in a glass cabinet catches my attention. It states the following, 'If you seek, you shall find. Enlightenment is knowing the truth.' After careful self-observation and divine guidance by spiritual masters, I have come to understand one thing, which Jethi too has engraved deep into our hearts. In her calm voice Jethi once told us, 'My dears, remember what I am about to say. All human beings have the ability to reach the Buddha's state of mind. You do not need to go looking for the Buddha. He is within you. The truth is scattered everywhere, only if you learn to recognize it.' This is a simple yet accurate way to understand life in all its glory. I have spent countless hours in The Elgin, lost in the ancient artefacts it holds, giving wings to my deep-rooted interest in history and antiquities. This room provides me solace when I want to escape the noise and chaos of living in a hotel. It is like a cloak of invisibility—my secret space. These walls help me escape from the rest of the world. It is my secret oasis where I can be alone with my thoughts, even if it is for a few minutes. At times of sorrow or even extreme happiness, I escape into this secret section of The Elgin.

This room of wonders is my home within a home. It transports me into a different time zone altogether. The Elgin is soaked in history; each hotel of ours has a unique foundation of its own, with a distinct story to tell. They have stood strong through countless years and changing times. Some have been the palaces of royal families, while others have a rich history of over two hundred years. Each one is an exquisite work of art in its own right.

If you wish to time travel, then do visit The Elgin for a Himalayan rendezvous.

11

THE MIDNIGHT WALK

On lone streets I walk, at peace with the silence, crossing the old clock tower as it strikes midnight. The tune sends a strong vibration throughout Darjeeling. The wolves howling in the moonlight sends a chill down my spine. The twinkling stars guide me in the darkness. The Mall Road in Darjeeling has never felt so enchanting. Cloaked in thick mist, the town feels gothic. I have nicknamed this 'my special route' as I make my way towards Jalapahar.

As I walk the endless path, I tremble because of the February chill. With a torch in one hand and an umbrella in the other, I observe the exquisite flowers that bloom only during the witching hour. The scent of the forest and the nocturnal flora and fauna encourage me to keep walking the distance. On a clear night, the Kanchenjunga can be seen glowing in the distance with no other light but that of the stars brightening up the snow-clad peaks—a sight so mesmerizing that one can sit quietly on the wooden benches of the pathway to witness God's marvellous creation. The night is full of mysteries in the Himalayas. Light from the small houses scattered across the mountains twinkle, merging with the glowing galaxies above. This is the charm of our land.

Walking slowly because of the rising altitude, we finally reach Jalapahar, which is known for its active army base and beautiful colonial homes that give it a historic essence in the modern world. The army has many cantonment zones within these mountains. Our borders adjoin Bhutan, Nepal and Bangladesh. The state of Sikkim borders Tibet in China. Therefore, the presence of the armed forces is of utmost importance for the government. I usually walk up this road with my parents and make a pit stop at the house of a dear friend of my father's, who is a high-ranking military general. The army also helps to avoid encroachment and destruction of our natural ecosystem, stopping the place from becoming a concrete jungle, which is a blessing for us.

If you look through the trees carefully, you might spot different species of nocturnal creatures in their natural habitat. The roving eyes of these forest dwellers can spook and enchant you at the same time. I am usually on the lookout for new species of nocturnal flora and fauna whenever I am with Papa. His knowledge of the land is unbeatable.

My father says, 'Can you smell that in the air...a sweet scent? The trees that bloom in the dark are known as *raat ki rani*, the queen of the night. They fill the terrain with their intoxicating scent for miles on end. We have one growing in our hotel in Kalimpong too. The speciality of this flower is that it only blooms at night. The pure white bloom, in all its glory, lets out a natural perfume that you can never miss. It's the flower of Aphrodite.' My father is my guide in the wilderness as he explains the significance of every flower. He says, 'This is my passion in life.'

It is no wonder that the gardens he has created in his hotels are a sight to behold. When walking with me at midnight, he says, 'I love flowers, and I like to surround myself with them. Whether it be spring, summer, autumn or winter, my gardens are always a burst of colours. Whether it be night or day, my gardens always have something extraordinary to share.' Our gardens also have strange visitors that may come as a surprise. And they may visit not just the gardens. Midnight walks can turn into midnight missions when living in the mountains.

It is one such night with a crescent moon when Mama and Papa are engrossed in a conversation on the balcony about renovations at the hotel, but something makes them pause. I see a strange black thing fall from the roof and crash onto the floor next to me. Sitting right opposite my father, I am startled and jump straight towards him. 'Papa! What in the world is that? It is on the floor,' I shout.

My father rises quickly from the sofa and moves towards the source of noise. He says, 'It is a bat. Quick, Nimmi, call the reception at once. Oh, look! It is a baby bat. Poor thing is hurt. It seems more terrified of us than the other way around.'

My mother springs into action and brings a bowl of water from her room. She quickly says, 'Diamond, let us give the poor animal some water; it might help for now. The baby bat has hurt its right wing. Let's not crowd around and make it feel threatened.'

'Oh my, it has such a small face; it looks so innocent,' my mother says, behaving like a fearless Goddess, pouring water—a drop at a time—into its mouth. Soon, the tiny animal seems to calm down. It rests its small dark wings on the white marble floor.

'Nimmi, it looks highly unlikely that the bat would fly any time soon. What should we do now? We cannot leave it out here in the open balcony to be hunted. The cats roaming at night will have a field day. We have to move it to safety or make some other arrangements. Wait a minute, I have an idea,' my father says, disappearing from the balcony. In a few minutes, I see a large netted cover used for fruit bowls in his hand.

'Step aside, ladies. I have just the thing to rescue this

little fellow.' My father gently covers the frightened little bat with the large net dome. The fruit bowl cover turns into a makeshift safety net. 'That should keep it safe till morning.' We all breathe a sigh of relief.

Soon dawn arrives. It is 6 a.m. I set an alarm to check on the little bat. The thought of it kept me awake in bed till late at night. Our night guard had not just been patrolling the premises but was also in charge of looking out for the little creature. I grab my robe and walk through the open corridors all the way to the balcony. To my surprise, I see my mother already standing next to the bat.

'Good morning, sweetheart. You are up early. I could not sleep well too. I am here to check on our little guest,' she says while sipping on some coconut water. She slowly moves a strand of my hair behind my ear and tidies the collar of my night suit when she spots our bellboy, Shankar, in the distance. 'Shankar! Shankar! Could you come up to the balcony please?' she says out loud, then she quietly whispers in my ear, 'Rea, at this point, he is the only man who is good with wild animals within the hotel. I hear stories of his daring encounters with poisonous snakes back in his village. I'm sure he can handle a little bat with care. Let's give it a go.'

Shankar quickly walks up the stairs and heads straight towards the little bat.

'We need your help. It's a rescue mission. Can you see the little animal gripping tightly onto the net? It looks like it's terrified yet seems in a much better condition than last night,' my mother says, holding onto my hand tightly. To our surprise, Shankar—who otherwise looks timid—transforms into a fearless person. He grabs the net effortlessly and places it on the bark of our mango tree. As soon as Shankar turns the net around, the little bat removes its claws and flies away to freedom.

'Wow, Shankar, well done! Well done, indeed! You are an expert at this,' Mama says in absolute joy. 'Rea, do you know that this is a good omen? To rescue a bat, especially by giving it water with your own hands is a very auspicious sign. Papa and I were discussing it last night too. We have never given an injured wild bat water up close like this before. It was quite an experience for us. In ancient myths of the land, bats signify rebirth and renewal. It is a sign of letting go of the old while paving the way for the new. From today, all negativity will fade away from our lives. I have a good feeling about this. Come, let's go and relish the breakfast buffet since we are up already. I do want some baked beans and sunny side up on this bright day.'

'You know, this encounter with the wild reminds me of our many midnight strolls around town. I clearly remember a romantic walk with your father a week after our wedding day. We barely knew each other then. It seems like yesterday though. Diamond and I walked hand in hand when we spotted countless Himalayan owls in the darkness of the forest. Diamond surely has an eye for spotting wildlife. It was a part of him that I was unaware of back then. I was newly married after all. Your grandfather allowed us to go on a single coffee date, even after we were engaged, that too accompanied by my two aunts. Privacy was out of the question. I know this may seem odd to you now, but times were different back then. Anyway, that night was special and an auspicious one too. We spotted the most spectacular beauty in the wild—a snow-white owl seated on a hollow tree trunk with its eyes closed, almost glowing in the pitch-dark coniferous trail. You can spot these shy creatures by following their sound as they call out in the moonlit night. This was the night I fell in love with Diamond!' my mother says, reminiscing about her younger days.

12

THE GOLDEN STUPA

Darjeeling is also influenced by the Japanese in the form of the Golden Stupa, which is roughly a thirty-minute drive away. Situated on the slopes of the Jalapahar hills, its distinct architecture and sleek design stand out among the various petite houses and Tibetan monasteries. My mother and Mrs Plant, on a spontaneous trip, take me to this place.

My mother, the religious one in our clan, somehow always finds herself in sacred spaces. Her energies are drawn to such sights for reasons I may never know. Dressed in black cashmere overcoats and elegant Indian sarees, the two women guide me on this journey.

'Mrs Plant, come and feel the tranquillity surrounding this place!' my mother says to her partner in crime. 'These white stupas have shining golden domes at the top, which is in complete contrast to the simplicity of its white structure. Look how the dome glitters when the morning light touches its smooth surface. Magnificent! On a clear day I can spot this golden dome from a distance. I have a clear view of the stupa from my bedroom window.

'The people of Darjeeling are dependent on the ever-changing weather of the Himalayas for their livelihood, and definitely for a good view. As the grey clouds shift and the clear blue sky becomes visible again, the hearts of the Himalayan people shine bright, and we head out and explore our wilderness. I personally love the summer months, yet my heart secretly longs for the October skies. A cluster of birds fly overhead forming a V in the sky. The Japanese stupas look like something straight out of a postcard—picture-perfect.' My mother enchants us as we make our way into the main hall of meditation.

I walk into the silence and recall something from my past at this very spot. The voice of Mrs Plant speaking to me...in another time...somewhere in the past. The smell of lemongrass fills the room as I walk down memory lane.

Mrs Plant is asking me a question. 'What do you wish for, Rea? Light this candle and make a wish. It is Children's Day today, and all the wishes of children will be granted!' I visualize myself as an eight-year-old, and hear myself speak, 'I wish to become Miss Universe one day.'

Coming back to the present, I walk towards Mrs Plant and say, 'Aunty Shirley, do you remember our last visit here?'

Her memory is very sharp. She says, 'Yes, I remember it clear as day! You made a wish to become Miss Universe. Rea, you couldn't even pronounce it at that age, but said, "Aunty Shirley, I wish to become Miss Nuniverse," with your missing front tooth. It was so adorable!'

I giggle slowly and say, "I guess my wish didn't manifest after all. I could not reach the minimum height requirement for the pageant. I am only five feet two.'

Mrs Plant notices my dimming eyes and says, 'No, dear, your dream has manifested. Your wish has been granted. You are the 'universe's child'! A step up from the crown. You have its compassion. My dear, you must grasp the true essence of inner knowledge. Do look out for the signs that are often hidden in plain sight. The golden stupas stand separate from the Tibetan monasteries that are scattered all over the terrain. This is a stand-alone star of the Japanese culture in our Himalayan home. I come to this spot very often as it fills my heart with peace. I always look out for tranquil places because it keeps my heart chakra and mind in cosmic harmony—it creates a soothing effect. I usually sit on the wooden bench overlooking the stupa for a while and lose track of time. Gazing at the open coniferous forest behind the stupas gives me a sense of peace. No wonder they call this place the "Peace Pagoda".

'The Peace Pagoda was built by the Japanese Buddhist Order of the Nipponzan-Myōhōji. The temple houses four different avatars of the Buddha. As one enters the grounds, there is a temple with a spectacular golden statue of the Buddha, and you can see a towering white pillar as you descend inside. It is spacious and a perfect spot to meditate.'

My mother grows quiet for a moment and then begins to shed light on her personal experience around these forests. I walk down her memory lane, almost like I was with her at that moment in time. She says, 'I have been witness to the strong vibrations of these forests. One evening, when Diamond and I were driving back from Kalimpong to Darjeeling, something strange happened. You know very well how Diamond is on the road late in the evenings. He is swamped with work throughout the day with someone or the other catching hold of him. How that still irritates me! Well, our journey to Darjeeling was going just as planned till we reached an unexpected sharp bend that the chauffeur couldn't see clearly; it was a foggy evening. Suddenly, the chauffeur hit the brakes. I was dozing off in the back seat of the car. The car smashed into a nearby rock; my car door flew open and I was thrown out. It was nearly sundown as I rolled down the tumbling woods and came to a sudden stop. I was disoriented and in a state of shock but slowly regained my footing. Diamond was running towards me. He saw me at a distance, standing near a large tree, and called out to me in panic, "Nimmi! Nimmi, can you hear me?" He said out loud but I couldn't move an inch. I was frozen in place. My vision was starting to get dark but then, something miraculous happened. I saw my ascended master standing in front of me. It was a vision of my guru giving me strength in my time of distress.'

'Diamond reached me and called out to me again. He shook me a couple of times but got no reaction out of me. He was left with no other choice but to slap my face to get me out of my state of shock. That was the only time when your father resorted to such a thing. I felt my guru's vision slowly disappearing, giving way to the bright light of reality. It felt as if I was waking up from a dream-like state and I held your father tightly.

'The accident seems like it happened yesterday. I remember every little detail to this day. It happened somewhere in these mysterious woods. I am certain there is something powerful in these forests.

'Legend has it that this is an important area for a group of individuals who follow the order of the sacred masters. A group of people who are very discreet in their workings. With unknown identities, their main focus is to spread unity and work towards a collective consciousness of the planet— the message of patience, peace, kindness and love. The sacred masters live in an alternate dimension, in an etheric plane—a mythical land of Gods and Goddesses, a seat of enlightened beings called "Shambhala" meaning "the source of happiness" in Sanskrit. The gateway of Shambhala opens only for people who are worthy, based on their karma. Buddhists believe it lies deep within a valley, surrounded by tall glaciers. Sweet nectar from the rivers of Shambhala flows through the valley. The capital city of Kalpa lies within the centre of the palace, which is shaped like a lotus. The air is filled with the sweet scent of sandalwood. It is the land of peace and immortality—a seat of a divine lineage of the 'Kalki Kings', the kings of dharma.

'Ancient legends prophesy a time when the planet will be thrown into chaos and war, and the twenty-fifth ruler of Shambhala will ride out from its gates to bring about a golden era. A new dawn on earth. Himalayan yogis call it "Gyanganj", a place holding spiritual teachings. A sacred space with "the tree of life" connecting the heavens, the earth and the underworld, balancing the flow of energy in the different planes.'

My mother takes me into the land of immortals. These forests depict an outer beauty with an inner strength and they spread the message of peace. This is the reason why I visit this transcendental space, especially at a time when there is so much suffering and pain in the world.

13

TALES OF TENZING

The Himalayas are a playground for those who love to push their limits. This is why I adore the natural landscape. Adventure runs deep in my veins. I can feel it pulsing in my body. My father takes me deep into the world of Tenzing as snow starts to fall outside.

Watching the falling snow, Mr Diamond says, 'The famous man from our hills who dared to be the first person to conquer the highest peak in the world is Tenzing Norgay. His footsteps made history, his fame spreading to all corners of the globe like a storm. He is the godfather of mountaineers. History recognizes Tenzing Norgay as the first man to shed light on the highest unconquered peak in the world. For Tenzing's extraordinary bravery, we celebrate his conquest here in Darjeeling.'

My father has dedicated the Tenzing Norgay wing at The Elgin to honour his legacy. His son, Jamling Tenzing Norgay, is a living legend and is a dear friend of our family. My father hands me a photograph and says, 'This is a photograph of your grandfather and Tenzing Norgay at Darjeeling. I keep it close to my heart as a part of our family legacy. That reminds me—I must give a copy of this photograph to Mr Jamling. He would love it.'

With the black and white picture on my lap, I hear my father share stories of the past. 'Tenzing Norgay was born in Nepal in May 1914 and passed away on 9 May 1986 in Darjeeling. *TIME* hailed him as one of the hundred most influential people of the twentieth century. Tenzing's mausoleum stands in Darjeeling's serene lap in the Himalayan Mountaineering Institute (HMI). Mountaineers from all around the globe come to Darjeeling to pay their respects to this legendary Sherpa. Near his grave is a palm tree, which is surprisingly tall and stands strong in this cold misty Himalayan terrain. Palm trees normally grow in lower tropical altitudes in hot and humid weather. This is the reason why the people of Darjeeling consider this palm tree in the high Himalayas an unusual occurrence, thus giving it the name, "Tenzing's Tree".

'There is also a stone tablet placed on his memorial, engraved with his words, *You cannot be a good mountaineer, however great your abilities, unless you are cheerful and have the spirit of comradeship.* His son, Mr Jamling, lives among us and continues the legacy of his father. I had invited him to inaugurate the Tenzing Norgay wing and share some incredible stories of the bewildering mountains. Following in his father's footsteps, Mr Jamling has climbed the summit of Everest multiple times. He has gifted The Elgin many artefacts and pictures that are priceless, and have never been seen by the public. A signed copy of his book, *Touching My Father's Soul,* is kept in our archives, gifted by Mr Jamling.'

My father continues, 'My dear, it is with great honour that we hold these Himalayan relics, which include original photographs of Edmund Hillary and Tenzing Norgay together at the summit, the birthplace of Tenzing in Nepal, Jawaharlal Nehru with Tenzing Norgay and his family on the former's visit to HMI, the flag hoisted by Norgay on the summit of Everest and Sherpa Tenzing with Kuldip Chand Oberoi.'

Mr Norgay shared a cordial relationship with my grandfather, Kuldip Chand Oberoi, and the memory of their friendship is kept alive in our home. Thus, the Tenzing wing is special to us. We have heard many tales about the expedition to Everest while living here in Darjeeling.

On Christmas Eve, Mr Jamling sits with us for dinner and brings some more of his tantalizing tales to the table. The grilled chicken is brought to the Duke Hall. He begins, 'For Sherpa Tenzing, it was like stepping into an alien world when he first reached the Everest summit. The Himalayas can be a very dangerous yet serene place.' As the dinner goes on, my sister Aanyaa raises a glass at the table and says, 'Let's stir up the night with yet more legends about this unknown land, shall we? Do regale us with the legends of Everest.'

My father too raises his glass of Bordeaux and immediately takes over the conversation, allowing Mr Jamling to eat his dinner. With a mouthful of chicken à la Kiev, questions start bouncing around the table.

'The tale that fascinates us all is that of the mysterious Himalayan yeti. This mythical creature is believed to live on the snow-clad mountains, wandering its high slopes. This creature is, in the real sense, larger than life. Massive footprints, believed to be of the yeti, were spotted in the Himalayas, and this is the story we have heard our entire lives. The name, Big Foot, is given to this creature in Western cultures for good reason. It is ten times an average human's size. Some mountaineers have even encountered the yeti at Everest. They say it remains camouflaged by the snow and is impossible to spot. Almost as if it is wearing an invisibility cloak on the snow-white slopes. This creature is believed to be one of the guardians of the sacred summit of Everest—its protector. Local folklore comprises stories of different types of yetis that roam the Himalayas, such as a creature called the "Nyalmo", which is one of the commonly known yetis in the snow-clad mountains. Legend has it that the mythical land of Shambhala has two guards at its gates. Shambhala's gatekeepers are believed to be two towering yetis, strong as the mountains itself,' my father says while taking a sip of his wine.

He continues, 'The mysteries of Everest do not end there. They have just begun. I have heard mountaineers speak of the dead. Tales of Everest speak of phantom men who help climbers up the unforgiving slopes. Shadows follow and guide mountaineers through snow storms and avalanches. Some say it is the lack of oxygen at these high altitudes that causes hallucinations among climbers, while some swear by its authenticity. Many believe these are real encounters. One can only wonder, but the mystery remains. The HMI in Darjeeling holds many extraordinary tales in its museum's archive. A tour of the HMI should be on everyone's bucket list, especially mountaineers and adventure seekers. A rock-climbing adventure up the steep "Tenzing Rock" awaits anyone looking for an adrenaline rush to spice up their holiday. It is a perfect blend of history and adventure that caters to the likes of many thrill seekers. This is the land of the "Tiger of the Snows", Tenzing Norgay.'

14

THE SACRED TREE

The crimson flowers of the rhododendron, locally called 'lali guras', are sacred to us in the Himalayas. They turn Darjeeling into the 'Garden of the Hesperides'. Besides its overwhelming beauty, the trees have medicinal properties, thereby making them highly valued. These delights only grow specifically in the cold Himalayan terrain, making it our sacred tree.

Oh, and there are hill after hill of wild rhododendrons as I enter the land of the thunderbolt in the month of March. It's 11 a.m. on my watch and I strongly feel Lady Winter's changing moods. The thick ice on the land has melted, but the winds are yet to warm up. I sit under the oldest and wisest tree inside our premises. This crimson lady has been my companion growing up. It has stood by me through turbulent nights of gusting monsoon winds and romantic mornings where I scribbled love notes on paper. I call her 'Scarlet', my floral friend. The Elgin has three of these trees standing tall on their premises. You cannot miss them, as my oldest friend guards the entrance beside the golden gate.

I can feel the soft grass on my bare feet as I look up into Scarlet's wooden maze. Her strong branches merge into one another, supporting the delicate flowers. With a pen and paper in hand, I draw the bark in the first stroke and let nature inspire me. Jethi strolls into the garden and spots me under the red umbrella of the rhododendron. Dressed in another one of her Tibetan bakhus, she picks up her pace and joins me.

'There you are, Rea! Enjoying the cold, I see. Let's get a cup of hot tea, shall we? Or even better, let's have something else. It is the season after all. Look how our sacred tree blooms.' Jethi tiptoes in her black leather pumps towards Scarlet's thick branches. My nanny's five-foot-tall body can reach great heights when she wills it to. Raising a wide napkin in the air, Jethi gently shakes the tree's branches and collects a few of Scarlet's flowers in her left hand. She picks one and without any warning puts it into my mouth. 'Here you go, Rea! This will do for the time being.' She quickly grabs another flower and begins to chew on it herself. 'And one for the road,' Jethi says to me while making her way back to the kitchen. This is our little Himalayan tradition.

Rhododendrons bloom specifically in the windy months of March through mid-April. These flowers are a sign of hope and prosperity, signalling the end of winter and the arrival of spring. This is the best time to celebrate nature's gift of transformation.

In the distance, I can see my father inspecting the grounds with an army of gardeners following his strict instructions. 'Hello, my sweetheart. Enjoying the bloom and the fresh air? As I have caught you under our red umbrella, I will come join you for a while.' His voice breaks the silence of the garden. 'This one is my personal favourite, Rea. Just look at the size of its flowers. Rhododendrons grow at high altitudes of above 4,000 feet, making them a Himalayan speciality. The rhododendron is not only the national flower of Nepal but also the sacred flower of the Himalayas. I eagerly wait for it to bloom as I take a few of these beauties to your grandmother every morning. You know she suffers from asthma. It runs in the family, so you should take it with a pinch of salt. The healing properties of rhododendrons are known to prevent and cure various ailments of the human body, such as asthma, bronchitis issues, headaches, fever, constipation, dysentery and various diseases associated with the heart. It is an excellent antioxidant to refresh the body. The best part of the flower is that it is easy to consume. Your Badi Mama can chew on them with ease. Its edible nature makes the flower popular. Many a time while walking home after strolling around town, I pluck a flower from the tree in the Duchess Garden and casually chew on it,' my father says, stretching his hand out towards the flowers.

Jethi should be credited for inculcating this behaviour in all of us. She taught us the unique ways of using the rhododendron and its countless properties; the tangy taste of the flower grows on you with time. I still wait eagerly for March to witness these red ladies bloom so I can admire their beauty and relish their tangy taste. In addition to its various medicinal benefits, it supports the body's natural detoxification process. The pickled flower can last for months at a time, making it highly durable. Rhododendron juice is considered a delicacy in the Himalayan mountains.

Apart from eating it raw, there are various forms in which you can use this miraculous flower. A cup of hot rhododendron tea is a soothing delicacy. Jethi is in the kitchen, preparing rhododendron tea, which is an all-rounder and a crowd favourite. The local Sherpa community integrate the rhododendron into their daily lives for many purposes. Jethi, a proud member of the Sherpa clan, knows her way around the land. The flowers are also used as offerings to Hindu deities in temples across the region.

These are also widely used by the Himalayan forest shamans, the jhakris, in their sacred ceremonies. Mr Butler, our in-house forest shaman, performs rituals of removing nazar (evil eye) from our body with the help of the rhododendrons. Once a month, when the moon is at its fullest, he performs his ritual. Mr Butler picks a couple of flowers and moves them from our crown chakra on the head all the way to the lowest chakra, in slow circles, six times. With his eyes closed, I watch our shaman transcending into a higher dimension. He picks a few grains of raw rice from his black hat while softly humming a mantra to remove the effects of the evil eye on us. I have observed our shaman using not just the petals but the leaves too for his ritual. The jade green leaves of these magnificent trees can be used for various purposes. I am captivated as our shaman takes its leaves and slowly turns them into a soft paste. He mixes some droplets of water to smoothen the texture.

The medicine man says, 'This paste is used to naturally cure headaches in the Himalayas. These forests have a cure for everything. You just need to know where to look.'

I observe Mr Butler as he applies the soft paste on his forehead with his rough fingertips. He swears by the healing abilities of the rhododendrons. Mr Butler lays his right hand on its wooden trunk and touches the wise tree softly. He shuts his eyes to concentrate and goes into deep meditation. Then, bowing in front of the sacred tree, Mr Butler removes his black hat, which is adorned with a tiny Gorkha kukri or knife brooch. 'This is a sign of respect towards our natural doctors,' he says, whispering quietly into the thick tree trunk. From one healer to another, Mr Butler calmly says, 'Dhanyabad' or 'Thank you', and touches his forehead to the bark of the tree, thereby activating his ajna chakra.

'Rea, you must respect all living things, no matter what form they take. It may be a germinating seed or an adolescent tree. The essence of life is what keeps us together.'

Our forest shaman takes a tiny knife and removes an extract from the bark of the sacred tree. He whispers, 'This extract from the rhododendron is used to cure biological ailments such as coughs and dysentery. We mountain dwellers know how to make conscious use of the flora and fauna in our terrain. We believe in cosmic equilibrium—a balance between the purpose, matter and spirit of all things. We use "jari booti" or herbs provided to us by Mother Nature and believe that if we respect the animals and trees growing around us, nature will find a way to heal our worldly ailments and sorrows.'

Lost in botanical magic, I live its reality while a strong aroma starts pulling me in another direction. Jethi stands with a silver tray in hand, with some bubbling hot crimson tea in it. It is time to drink the nectar of the Sacred Tree, which will recharge and revitalize me. Mr Butler and Jethi lie under the rhododendron to feel its essence flow through them. I can feel the wet earth on my fingertips. Mr Butler slips into deep meditation; humming an ancient shamanic chant, he asks me to do the same. In his soothing voice, Mr Butler says, 'Close your eyes and drift away into the distant galaxies. Feel your body shift and move into the cosmos, away from all worldly attachments. Leave the earth behind. Now let my voice be your guide in space.'

I follow the shaman's voice, deep into the universe, away from our solar system.

'Can you see anything? What can you hear? Let your senses guide you.' Mr Butler takes me away from gravity. He whispers, 'Rea, can you hear a sound? A constant sound? Almost like deep breaths?'

I stay absolutely still for a while and then reply, 'Yes, Mr Butler. I can hear a strong, heavy yet calm sound flowing through the universe. What am I hearing?'

Butler clears his throat and guides me through it. 'It is the sound of the universe. One can hear this sound when in deep meditation. It sounds like our mantra, "OM", a constant "OM" flowing through the universe. It is as though the universe is breathing. Our universe is constantly expanding, with no end in sight. This is why it's impossible to tell how big the universe actually is. Feel its expansion in your atomic body. Expand and grow with it.'

The shaman takes me on a tour of a faraway galaxy, while our feet are still planted here on earth. I feel these crimson beauties turn into the 'Tree of Life', stretching the branches of my consciousness into the ever-expanding cosmos.

15

BORN IN THE EMBRACE OF THE THUNDERBOLT

As my twenty-ninth birthday approaches, I gaze towards the sapphire blue mountains where I first opened my eyes to experience this wonderland named Earth. Standing on the doorstep of thirty, I feel the mysteries of the upcoming year surround me, which brings with it mixed feelings of joy and fear. 'Gosh! How has the past decade flown by so quickly? I still feel like I have so much more to tick off my bucket list.' I nudge Aanyaa while scratching my right arm nervously. I have lived by the motto *mens regnum bona possidet,* or 'an honest heart is a kingdom in itself'. So I am being brutally honest with myself, accepting the arrival of my thirties.

'This is the beginning of real adult life, Rea. Honestly speaking, I feel we only truly mature at this particular time in our lives...mentally and emotionally,' my older sister speaks from experience.

I was born on 11 May, and the Roman Goddess Maia is my presiding deity. Under the Taurus constellation of the zodiac, my destiny unfolds. It is a month of rejuvenation and fertility, especially in my Himalayan home Darjeeling. One of the oldest hospitals in town—Mathew Hospital (within the grounds of the famous clubhouse)—has heritage status, just like most of the stone structures of the land. The comedy called life began in this hospital for me, where I arrived as an unplanned last child. The youngest member of the family is perhaps a surprise gift, always arriving at the end. They called me 'the love child' as I came with no warning. My mother came to know of my existence three months after I was conceived, right in the middle of her brother's wedding. It seemed like I had picked an auspicious moment to inform them of my arrival. Almost like a tap from within the womb saying, 'Mama... Hello! I am here. Can you hear me?'

I did not cause any trouble while in the womb, but I turned out to be quite a handful as I grew up. Whoever was born at the hospital in the year 1991 is well versed with the term 'Caesarean Scot'. My mother still tells the tale with a half-hearted smile. My mother, who is a software engineer, instantly detected a glitch in her system. Her brain is like that of a supercomputer, which is sometimes quite disadvantageous for us notorious bunch of siblings. She says, 'Come, Rea, I must tell you a funny story. Do you know most of the children born on that day were caesarean births, and the doctor became the talk of the town, which gave him the nickname of "Caesarean Scot"? It doesn't end there. The doctor would come over to The Elgin every other day to change my bandages. You know how much I longed to be a doctor, so I found it rather amusing. I remember telling Diamond that isn't the doctor's visits a bit too frequent. It seems he has grown too fond of the spread of cakes and customary whisky laid out for him.'

I pause for a brief moment and finally get the joke. 'You can't be serious Mama. I can't believe my ears. How have you not mentioned this before?'

Sipping on her Darjeeling tea, she uncovers the large scar beneath her belly button and says, 'Quite a late reaction, my sweetheart. Look over here. This is how you came out of my womb. It reminds me of that doctor each time I look at my scar. Anyway, all is well that ends well.' She places her hands on my right cheek and gives me a loving look. We have a good laugh together as my mother takes me down her memory lane.

'You three children are a part of my body. My own flesh and blood. There is no bond more sacred or pure than that of a mother and child. It is the ultimate truth,' she says with pride in her voice. 'I can do anything for my kids.' My mother gives me a warm cuddle and holds me close. I can feel her unconditional love in that moment. A golden aura envelops us in its circular dome because of our embrace.

While I snuggle into her lilac cashmere sweater, I reveal something of my own. 'Mama, can I tell you a secret? I have never spoken about this with anyone, not even Aanyaa. It is something very personal to me,' I whisper to her and wait for her reply with my eyes closed.

Gently stroking the long locks of my hair, she says, 'Yes, my baby. You can tell me anything. Go on now. Let it all out.' She calms me with her gentle touch.

With my eyes still closed, I whisper, 'It is something that keeps me awake at night. Many people across the globe recall their first memory as that of being in the womb, especially while using techniques such as regression and meditation. But I recall something different. When I tune into my non-physical self, my consciousness takes me back into a moment in the solar system where I am a ball of fire crashing towards the Earth like an asteroid. I wonder if it is my first soul memory of pre-human birth—a moment that I can still recall when I sit in silence. Sometimes, I feel a strong attraction for the distant galaxies. I know that this is my home, the place of my birth is my home, yet I feel a deep-rooted longing to go "home", which is far away in the multidimensional galaxy.' Holding my mother tight, I reveal my inner thoughts to my creator.

My hometown has a special element. In the Himalayas, a name can reveal many things about a person or a place. A name is not just a name. 'Darjeeling' comes from the Lepcha words, 'Dorje' and 'ling', which translate to 'the land of the thunderbolt'. My Lepcha spiritual guide takes me deep into the land of the thunderbolt and its origins. Sitting on the floor with his legs crossed, I join Mr Butler, 'the forest shaman', while he begins his captivating oration. Holding a marigold flower in his hand, he says, 'According to Indian mythology, the Hindu God Indra's weapon is the thunderbolt. Legend has it that the king of heaven was pained by the destruction due to the violation of nature's law of living in harmony. Deadly weapons had caused an imbalance, which had created turmoil in the realms of heaven and man. The God of thunder dropped his powerful sceptre on earth to bring about peace in all the realms. His actions persuaded the other Gods to drop their weapons and instead focus on their moral duties of maintaining harmony in the land. Then, Lord Indra created a piece of heaven on earth and named it Dorje-ling. In the local language, "Dorje" means thunder, thus Darjeeling got its name—the land of the thunderbolt. It is evident as to why the land got this name, as it is blessed with rains, giving it plenty of water to sustain the gushing rivers, waterfalls and dense vegetation, filled with numerous flora and fauna. Our lands are brimming with natural treasures, which extend all the way to the people living on it. To be born in the land of the thunderbolt, high up in the Himalayas, is truly a blessing from the heavens.' He joins his hands and bows his head as a form of gratitude to the heavens above.

For me, being born in the sunny month of May is uplifting. This month adds more colours to our floral world. I look out of the windows and see that the Duchess Garden at The Elgin is filled with bright pink blossoms. Hydrangeas and trumpet lilies too signal the month of my birth. I look towards my sister lying on the comfortable ombré couch and say, 'Aanyaa, I have a quick question. What is your favourite flower?'

My sister gazes up at me and says, 'Hmm...let me think. I guess it's a rose—its scent and simplicity are what I love about it. Well, what about you, Rea?' I walk towards the flower vase and pick one up. 'Here, this one.'

With a blooming lily in my hand, I crush one of its orange petals and apply it to my sister's forehead. 'There you go, little Goddess. Lily symbolizes Hera, the Greek Goddess of marriage, women and family, and the protector of women during childbirth.'

I was born and brought up in these high altitudes and the most refreshing part of living here is the fresh Himalayan air and open landscape, which allow me to freely explore myself and my surroundings. The wild forest allows me to wander freely. Darjeeling provides ample room for physical and mental growth. With my legs up on the suede couch, seated right next to my sister, some long-lost memories emerge. 'Aanyaa, look at your legs. They're absolutely spotless.'

Aanyaa turns towards my legs and says, 'Rea, so are yours. Look, they're almost the same as mine.' I glance at my legs and point towards my right knee. 'Do you remember this scar? How it happened? I got four stitches that day. The mark hasn't gone from my knee till this day.'

Aanyaa unlocks her memory bank and says, 'Oh yes. Is that the same scar? How can I ever forget? You were really young then. Around ten or eleven years old. It had been a thunderous night and rain was lashing at us. You tripped on a large water pipe on the way back home. There was a deep cut on your knee, and blood was oozing from your leg. I was so terrified but I tried to be brave and came up with a solution. I gave you a piggyback ride home. You didn't stop crying the whole way. That night is a memorable one.'

I had a sly smile on my face and said, 'It surely was. It left a permanent mark on me.'

Darjeeling has numerous forests where I like to wander about, stream pools in which I like to take a dip and tea gardens that I love exploring as strong Himalayan winds allow my imagination to carry me to far-off lands without any boundaries. Just like the meaning of my name, 'Rea' (a tranquil river), I flow like snow-fed waters. Living in this terrain makes us mountain dwellers strong and hardy inside out. We may fall down countless times, but we learn to get back on our feet. We dance among ladybirds, fly with dragonflies and tango with bumblebees. We get lost under the dense canopy of oak trees, but find our way back home, like fireflies in the night. We are accustomed to the cold weather and high altitudes so the fear of heights has never been in our DNA. With the heart of a 'strong Sherpa', the soul of a 'forest shaman' and the appearance of my mortal creators, I stand strong as my masters—Butler, Jethi, Diamond and Nimmi—guide my path.

The fear of wandering around at night turns into a thrill of adventure as my sister and I set up camp in the arms of the open wilderness. As the night goes by, we sit by the blazing bonfires we have created. The fear of encountering Himalayan snakes hidden in tea bushes or coming in contact with bloodsucking leeches has never existed in *our* nature.

Getting stung by a bumblebee while admiring the blooming flowers or walking home in the silence of twilight through the million shortcuts we have discovered is part of normal everyday life. We grow up, hand in hand with nature, sharing this sacred space. Most of all, we do not consider ourselves separate from nature. We learn to understand the changing landscape and the fluctuations of the unpredictable weather.

I believe the most important thing for a human being is freedom, and Darjeeling provides the perfect backdrop for a rendezvous with Mother Nature. *Montani semper liberi* (mountaineers are always free) has been another motto of our lives.

'Aanyaa, we have been through thick and thin together, haven't we, since the day I was born. At least you have lived for six years before me. I wonder how that felt.' I giggle. Before I can catch my breath, Aanyaa has her answer. She pulls up the beige collar of her shirt and says, 'Oh no! My intuitive skills were quite sharp, even at the age of six. Before you were born, I was playing with Viraj's toy cars and soldiers. Boys are utterly boring, that's for sure. I remember telling Jethi that I wanted a younger sister to play with. Just like a little doll. I knew you would come. Especially for me.'

My giggles turned into a heartfelt moment. 'Then it makes us soul sisters,' I say, holding her soft hand. It is a brief moment of truth for us in the Himalayan silence. We are each other's strength. Being the granddaughter of a freedom fighter—on my mother's side—the sense to break free runs deep in my veins. My grandfather, Ganesh Das Khatri, taught us to fight for what is right and revolutionize the world with our ideas. Fighting for India's freedom, he became a hero for us. It was the beginning of my grandfather's political career in Delhi. Freedom is a gift we humans take for granted, but I am and always will remain thankful for my freedom. I value the people who fought not so long ago to give us this joy today. To be born in the embrace of the thunderbolt has shaped my personality to be as strong as Indra's lightning bolt and as steady as the Himalayan mountains.

16

TIGER HILL CALLS

It's 4 a.m., an unusual time for anyone to start their day with enthusiasm, but at The Elgin, the breakfast buffet is laid out to be relished. Swarms of people rush down the stairways. The scheduled wake-up calls from the reception desk ring loudly in each room. The wooden doors are swung open and closed multiple times by overenthusiastic guests, who are having a conversation while making their way down to the reception. Room service is rushing up with breakfast and rushing down with luggage.

'It's time for Tiger Hill!' I can hear the guests' excited voices. Watching the sunrise at Tiger Hill is an attraction for tourists, especially for those who love photography and snow. Tiger Hill is the highest point in the region, where the Senchal Temple is situated. The temple is built in the middle of a wildlife sanctuary well camouflaged by mighty rocks. It cannot be missed if you visit Darjeeling also because there is a serene lake surrounded by trees located at the very top of the hill that is fed by the waters of Himalayan springs. Senchal Lake is situated at a high altitude of 8,160 feet, making it seem like it is floating in the clouds. The lake is also a reservoir for Darjeeling and the nearby villages.

A mystery dwells in this temple, and it draws visitors from all around the world. Legend surrounds this hill as there are many tales about the temple's origins. I am drawn to its divine feminine energy and can feel the Goddess around me when I visit.

Mr Butler is my guide to this holy shrine. He says, 'Senchal gets its name from the word Singha (lion) and is the holy place of the residing Goddess Singha Devi. According to local legend, anyone who disturbs the sacred hill suffers a great deal of misfortune, sometimes also resulting in their unnatural death. The wrath of the Lion Goddess will uproot their lives. This is a tale that serves as a warning to anyone trying to disturb the ecosystem. Long ago, British settlers, who did not respect the residing Goddess, dared to hunt down a pair of swans in the waters of the holy Senchal Lake. The foreigners soon met with misfortune, resulting in their barracks being completely destroyed by gusting winds and storms on this sacred hill. My dear, the main temple ground holds a gigantic rock formation, which has carvings of female deities.'

At the entrance of the temple are two towering snow lions who stand guard with an enormous steel bell hanging in between the two structures. I visit Tiger Hill often, mostly on foot as the rejuvenating walk through various forest trails also provides amazing views of the valley. There is an array of wildflowers blooming along the pathway. Magnolias cover hill after hill, turning the valley white. My journey takes three to four hours from Darjeeling town, depending on the pace at which one is walking through the quaint pathways. I usually carry a picnic basket along, with sandwiches and chicken rolls, on my journey. I discover many beautiful spots along the way where one can enjoy the view of the rolling tea gardens, the untouched coniferous forests and the mighty Kanchenjunga.

There are numerous Tibetan shops selling hot noodles, vegetable soup, spicy potatoes and soft momos, along with some Tibetan delicacies, if you wish to stop over and try out some local street food.

I begin my journey early in the morning and walk at a slow pace as I have the entire day to enjoy the changing panorama of the mountains. Many people head to Tiger Hill to witness the breathtaking view of the sun rising above the Kanchenjunga range. The best part of it all is the sun's rays falling on Mount Everest. Whether it be nature enthusiasts from around the globe or local inhabitants, everyone equally enjoys the beauty.

I feel a whiff of cool breeze while bowing down to the Himalayan deities. I carry a basket of bougainvilleas into the Senchal Temple. Set apart from the chaos of everyday traffic, this temple is a tranquil haven, and the only sounds you hear are the whooshing of the cold wind and the chirping of exotic birds.

As I walk inside the temple grounds, passing the two snow lions guarding the gates, I come across a body of water that looks something like a miniature lake. At the centre of this lake is an idol of Lord Shiva, the ultimate destroyer in Hinduism. Ancient tales say that one must walk around this lake three times and throw a coin into its shallow waters while making a wish. I do the same.

My belief draws me here. If something is bothering me, or if I need a wish to be fulfilled, I visit this sacred place for my mind to be at ease. I light a rose candle near a small rock placed at the entrance of the temple and step into the holy grounds. One would find thousands of red bangles and ornaments laid out as offerings to the female deity in the one-kilometre walk to the main temple rock. Oil lamps light up the dark cave where the devi is worshipped. A dozen bells ring when the winds crash into them. The resident pandit chants holy mantras and applies a tika to my forehead. He takes my right hand and ties a holy thread on my wrist—a thread of protection. With my eyes closed, I pray to the divine feminine and absorb the energy of the holy mantras into my being.

A call for peace is sent out into the wild as the pandit utters the words 'Shanti...shanti...shanti'. I feel a divine connection with the devi. This is my very own sacred space in the Himalayas; the vibration here uplifts me and keeps my mind, soul and heart aligned with nature's exuberance.

17

THE ELGIN'S LAUGHING BUDDHA

The Elgin has a rich heritage comprising artefacts, traditions and stories of the past. Similarly, the people within our walls are what makes The Elgin special. Concrete structures can be created and demolished as time passes, but the people and memories will stay forever.

One of our beloved personalities here is 'The Elgin's Laughing Buddha', a nickname the management has bestowed on this person with love. The tales of the 'Laughing Buddha' go back centuries in Eastern mythology. As I stroll into the lobby, my gaze falls upon a statue of one complementing the ambience. Unlike any other organization, we have a live laughing Buddha within our premises.

Why does the Buddha laugh? Many people do not know the significance behind his perpetual laughter. They simply admire it and consider it a good luck charm. Visitors buy a figurine from antique Tibetan shops and keep them as collectables, and display them in their homes as a souvenir, a memory. As legend goes, you should rub the tummy of the Laughing Buddha thrice, in a clockwise direction, and make a wish. By rubbing the big round belly of the Laughing Buddha, luck will be bestowed on you. So people usually follow this custom and keep the artefact in their homes as a luck bearer, but no one really knows why the Buddha is continuously laughing.

This was a question that rang in my mind, so I went to the person who I knew for certain could address my queries.

'Papa!' I say out loud as I walk towards his office, full of questions. 'I want to ask you something that has been on my mind since this morning. I realize we have a collection of Laughing Buddhas in the hotel, and one is even kept on top of your rolltop desk in the study. I know they are a sign of good luck, but I still have questions.'

With a gold pen and diary in hand, Mr Diamond says, 'What do you want to know, Rea?' He gazes at me through his frameless spectacles while in the middle of his paperwork. 'Go on, ask your question so I can answer it. I know the history behind each and every artefact in my hotel. You know very well that I do not accumulate objects without fully understanding the significance behind them, don't you?'

I say, 'That is the reason I have come to you.' I stand facing him. 'Please tell me, why does the Buddha laugh?' I get straight to the point.

'Come here and sit down,' he says.

I pull up a chair across from him, eager to listen to what he has to say.

'There is a simple message behind the Buddha's laughter. He laughs because tomorrow may bring anything with it. If you are happy and look at the Buddha, he laughs with you. If you are sad and look at the expression of the Buddha laughing, it signifies that this sorrow will not last forever. The Laughing Buddha is trying to convey the eternal truth that "tomorrow is another day" and no emotion continues forever. Everything is temporary in our lives. With his laughter, the Buddha says to us that happiness and sorrow are two sides of a coin. Just like the active day and relaxing night. Life is ever-changing. So, my dear, if you are sad or happy, you should live in the moment as tomorrow is a new day, bringing with it a new flux of emotions. Rea, this is the significance of the Laughing Buddha. This is why I have one on my rolltop desk to remind me that change is the only constant in life. This is why I have a hearty laugh and smile each day, knowing that tomorrow will be a more exciting and fascinating day. Whatever life brings to me, I take it with a smile and gratitude.'

I am overwhelmed by my father's words. It makes me stop worrying about everything; I will no longer let my emotions govern my life. Tomorrow is a new day. This makes me realize how wise my father really is, and together with the management team of The Elgin, we gave the name of 'The Elgin's Laughing Buddha' to the head of the organization, Mr Diamond Oberoi.

18

THE LIVING GODDESSES

The mighty mountains have been an abode for heavenly beings since the beginning of time. Mysticism and nirvana are connected with the Himalayan range. My home is dominated by strong feminine energies.

I recall a private conversation with our in-house forest shaman that always takes me into the depths of our land. After humming a soothing tribal mantra, Mr Butler had said, 'The Himalayas are home not just to us but to the living Goddesses, unique in every essence. Known as "Matas", these women have pure hearts and have a distinct aura that cannot be missed. Our people are the essence of the land. At a very young age, some girls are chosen to be the embodiment of Goddess Shakti. They are the chosen ones who begin to show signs of being touched by the devi. This has been a part of the Himalayan culture for centuries.'

Holding his aquamarine pendant in hand, the shaman had shifted his strong gaze towards the cloudy night sky. 'On a full moon night, sacred rituals are held in certain temples with the resident priest conducting a special ceremony. It is private, and only the town's people are in attendance. Powerful Goddesses, such as Saraswati, Durga and Kali, are evoked by the head priest, and these women act as a medium to communicate with us mortals. These women are known as the living Goddesses. It is believed that the Goddesses give their blessings and remove any ailment or problem that the villagers have by communicating with the locals during this sacred ritual. Rea, look up at the skies tonight. What a blessed night it is with the full moon in all its glory. The ceremony will begin at midnight. Would you like to see it for yourself? After all, it is an out-of-the-world experience.'

I paused for a moment and then let my intuition guide me.

'To the temple we shall go, Mr Butler,' I had said, excitement coursing through my veins. I had always wanted to attend a sacred ritual on a full moon night. Nothing could have been better than having a forest shaman to guide me through it. These traditions date back centuries and are carefully preserved to prevent them from getting lost with time.

'Let me share a little secret with you, hiding in plain sight. Within The Elgin, we have a lady in the housekeeping department who is also a "Mata". This may come as a complete surprise as she appears to be a simple lady, like any other member of our organization. Her name is Geeta. She is named after our sacred Hindu text. She surely lives up to her name by following a spiritual path. She keeps to herself most of the time. If you observe her carefully, you will see that she conducts herself in a different way. She does not interact much with others. You may have noticed her long tresses; the Goddesses never chop off their hair.'

I had asked Mr Butler if it was a regular occurrence. 'I wonder how Matas juggle their dual lives. I cannot make sense of it or figure out a reason for such duality. Is it not mandatory for them to keep away from the mundane world?'

Mr Butler had replied in a calm voice, 'The Matas maintain physical and social distance from us. They don't eat with us or interact with anyone of the opposite gender. They are strictly vegetarian and stay away from alcohol at all costs. They bring their own food and water. Matas, too, have to earn a living apart from being at the temple. Just like me. I, too, follow similar rules as a forest shaman but I work at the hotel to earn a living. It is all about the right balance, Rea.

'Remember to always have a balanced life, even when I am not around to remind you. Remember my words, my child. This is the beauty of the people of the hills. Ordinary people sometimes have extraordinary abilities. This is why one should never underestimate anyone or jump to conclusions based on their outer appearance.'

Mr Butler's voice had deepened as he continued, 'Goddesses are a symbol of power in our culture. They are a symbol of creation. Every woman has Devi Shakti's power within her.'

'Even me, Mr Butler?' I had asked quietly.

'Yes, even you, Rea!'

19

THE AWAKENED TARA

At every corner of the Himalayas, you will discover something so unique and fascinating that it's hard to place it in our modern world. Trust me when I say this. When you stand in these majestic, sacred mountains, you feel the air growing lighter; you can lose yourself in a realm of higher consciousness. Many people believe only in what their eyes can observe, and for those people, the Himalayas are the best place to see unbelievable things with your own eyes. The forces that exist in these hills can make even non-believers wonder as you can witness other-worldly phenomena for yourself.

Hidden deep in a little shrine lies a Goddess. A statue of the Green Tara.

'Green Tara' and 'White Tara' are two manifestations that branch out from the Lord Avalokiteśvara sect of Buddhism. Born out of the teardrops of the bodhisattva, these sister Goddesses are the embodiment of magic, knowledge, wealth and prosperity to the Himalayan people. 'Tara' in Sanskrit translates to 'star'. She is known as the Mother Goddess. Green Tara sits on a lotus that spreads its fragrance into the sweet night. The blooming lotus (or utpala) scatters her divine energy.

It is widely believed that a Green Tara statue located in Darjeeling has somehow come alive. People say that they have witnessed the face of Tara changing every time they visit the shrine to offer prayers. It is a surprising phenomenon. The position of the Tara keeps shifting, and so does her posture and the expression on her face. Sometimes her eyes are looking straight towards you, while at other times, the direction of her gaze has shifted. At times, her face is slightly bent towards the right, while at other times, it is bent towards the left. How is this possible? This statue of Tara has astonished people living here, resulting in rumours spreading like wildfire all through the district. How is it that a man-made statue can change its physical appearance? This bewilders everyone. *Goddess Tara seems to have awakened!* She is also well known as the 'wish-fulfilling Goddess' in Buddhist scriptures. Many devotees flock to her shrine to offer their prayers. It may sound unreal but this is something one has to witness for themselves.

I also have an urge to visit the shrine. The next morning, around 7 a.m., I begin my pilgrimage. I walk from Darjeeling, around twenty minutes downhill, and reach a quaint little shrine. There was a massive queue of believers, all of whom had offerings for the Green Tara in their hands. I could not contain my curiosity while standing among devotees stretching all the way to the railway tracks on Upper Hill Cart Road. As I stand there, I begin enquiring about the mysterious Green Tara.

The women are chanting, 'Om Tara, Om Tara' dressed in vibrant shades of dawn. I sense strong feminine energies encompassing me. A young lady wearing a white flower in her hair turns towards me and gives me the most comforting smile. I have impatience written all over my face as my hands are as cold as ice. I keep rubbing my palms together. This young girl asks me something out of the blue. She says, 'Stretch your hands and close your eyes.' I feel calm. 'Please trust me!' Her voice guides me, closing the doors of my vision, and I feel the gentle touch of the Goddess. A white lily is suddenly placed on my palms.

'Hello, my name is Tara,' the young girl discloses her identity in a sweet voice. I feel a strange sensation in my spine. Is this a sign? Am I being guided to the Goddess through this young girl named after Herself? I have a private conversation with the Green Goddess. The young girl begins to speak to me without hesitation. She says, 'Take this flower with you into the shrine and offer it to the Green Tara. Flowers are her favourite. She might grant your wishes immediately.' She holds a bundle of white lilies in her hands and adds, 'There is a saying that if you visit the shrine for four consecutive Thursdays, in the weeks to come, your wish will be granted. Is this your first Thursday? If it is, then I will give you the lay of the land. It is a simple practice, yet there is a small catch. If your wish is not meant to be fulfilled then the person offering prayers will not be able to reach the shrine the following four Thursdays. Something will keep you from visiting the shrine. Some work or the other will divert you. I have seen it happen. These miracles have been witnessed by many people and their belief in the Awakened Tara is unshakeable. This is the reason I am here too.'

As I make my way, slowly awaiting my turn, I glance towards the Awakened Tara to pray from a distance. 'What should I wish for?' I glance into the Goddess's emerald face. 'I wish for love and happiness for everyone on our planet.' I communicate in silence with the Goddess. As I move closer to her shrine, I feel something illuminating me from within. The statue of Tara seems to gaze straight at me. She holds a closed blue lotus (utpala) in her hands and is adorned with gold jewellery. Her eyes are half closed, but her third eye seems to be aware. I feel her calm energy surround me.

I am there for the collective good of our universe. I pray for this very thing on my visits to temples. I believe the ripples of a little pond can affect the tides of an entire ocean. It has the power to carry positive energy to every corner of the planet. To me, separation and togetherness are a state of mind. We are in a cosmic chain. A circle of life we live in while maintaining tranquillity, transformation and tender love.

'*Om tare tuttare ture soha!*' I pray to the Goddess of 'karuna' or compassion, and to 'shunyata' (void).

20

SANDAKPHU, BEYOND OUR WORLD

Sandakphu is a land somewhere above the clouds...quite literally! It is a trekker's ultimate paradise. Hiking on the Sandakphu trail is like taking a walk through clouds as it glides under my feet. Sandakphu lies in a strategic location between the two countries of Nepal and India, depicting a surreal beauty. Sandakphu Hill is the highest point in the state of West Bengal, where one can take one's subconscious a step higher in the Himalayas. The ecosystem of the land has distinct characteristics, setting it apart from the rest of the Himalayan belt.

I venture into the Himalayas, into the abode of Lord Shiva. On my thrilling trek up these secluded mountains with a local guide, I stumble upon a peculiar-looking plant.

'Wait a minute... What is that?' I say in a high-pitched voice that echoes all around in the silence of the terrain. I take a sudden leap forward and startle my guide walking ahead.

'Is that a snake? Goodness! It resembles a cobra. What is it supposed to be? These unusual plants are all around us. I have never seen one like this before!' I say, huffing and puffing on our uphill climb from the small hamlet of Meghma. My young guide bursts into sudden laughter, calming me down and filling my mind with curiosity. With a wooden stick and sour candy in his hand, my guide says, 'Madam, these are rare Himalayan plants. They grow here naturally in the wild. There is nothing to worry about. The cobra lilies of Sandakphu are something not many visitors are aware of. This endless stretch is the last concentration of Himalayan cobra lilies in the land. These cobra lilies are called "arisaema" in the local Nepalese language. Sandakphu got its name from these distinct lilies. The shape and structure of the plant most definitely resemble a cobra. Its green colour and the tentacles bulging out from the surface startle many mountaineers. You can admire it but I would advise you against touching it as they can prove to be very poisonous. This is nature's way of giving us a sign, by taking the shape of a deadly creature, that the plant is not to be meddled with. In fact, Sandakphu derives its name from the Tibeto–Burman Lepcha language and translates to "the mountain of poisonous plants". Don't be disheartened just yet. Snakes have a mysterious connection with the lord of the Himalayas. After all, we are heading towards the Sleeping Shiva.'

The next part of my Himalayan trek is laden with mountains full of rhododendrons. It is every trekker's delight to walk on stone pathways surrounded by these deep red trees till you reach the highest point on the route called Sandakphu. The trek continues through the picture postcard view of open woods, countless streams and scattered bridges. I walk on unknown lands and dream of Lord Shiva.

'Snakes and Shiva have an unbreakable bond. The Himalayas hold legends of Lord Shiva during the churning of the ocean, "Samudra Manthan". Ancient Vedas tell tales of the devas and asuras, Gods and demons, fighting over amrit, or the drink of immortality, when a poison capable of destroying the entire world emerged out of the milky ocean. Lord Shiva, being the all-powerful Lord, consumed the poison. In the depths of the ocean, a snake was drinking the poison along with him. This courageous snake melted Shiva's heart and he rewarded the snake by wearing it around his neck. The serpent, King Vasuki, holds a mythical gem called nagamani—a large diamond with magical powers. The snake is twirled three times around Lord Shiva's neck, signifying the past, present and future.' The young guide gives me the wisdom of the ages as I walk with the God of time.

A whiff of a sweet floral aroma carries me into Sandakphu towards the Sleeping Shiva. The guide pauses to quench his thirst at a flowing stream and says, 'Drink up, Madam. This stream is coming straight from the glaciers. Have a sip to see the difference.'

I drink from the clear stream and sprinkle some icy water on my face. 'Although its beauty is sublime, this trek is not for the faint-hearted because the constant rise in altitude can leave many breathless. I have heard of a handful of amateur trekkers climbing up the mountain too quickly without taking into consideration the rapid and sudden rise in altitude, which can prove fatal. Many have fainted on the trek due to lack of oxygen. People have even suffered severe brain damage and clotting of blood vessels. One has to stay the night at various trekking huts in the nearby villages to keep up with the terrain. Although, in our modern age, there are roads built on a separate path where off-road jeeps can take you to the highest village of Meghma. Visitors do take that route, but it does not compare to the beauty of the pathways through the Singalila National Park. They miss out on the best part!'

As I lose myself in the surrounding beauty, my guide suddenly breaks the silence. 'There is a serene walkway through the dense woods if you are interested in bird watching. I have ventured on these paths for over twenty years. I can help you spot some rare species of Himalayan birds. On one occasion, I stumbled upon a rare Himalayan spotted owl with its offspring in the middle of the day. If we are lucky, we can spot the endangered red pandas that are the most adorable creatures in these forests...and if we are unlucky, we may find a pack of wolves too!' His words frighten me, but his calm attitude and carefree smile manage to soothe my nerves at the same time.

Being a daredevil myself, I carry on with my journey. The smell of the forest guides me. Sandakphu is a thrilling trek for sure, and one that will leave you breathless, quite literally. The guide takes a long breath and says, 'Rea Madam, Sandakphu is known globally for offering a breathtaking sight that can only be witnessed from these hills. The four highest peaks in the world can be seen together in one frame as you reach the end point of the route—Everest, Kanchenjunga, Lhotse and Makalu.'

From a distance, it seems like Lord Shiva is resting with his hand folded on his chest, in a peaceful meditative form, frozen in the snow as though he might get up at any moment. Chewing on 'chhurpi', a yak's milk cheese that my guide shares with me, I notice a black dog following us. 'This little fellow has been our shadow through the trek. I think we changed ways long back. Can you please give me a biscuit for the little fellow?' I request the guide to treat our four-legged friend. There are three of us on the trek now.

I feel cushioned by the clouds. My guide says, 'These Himalayas are eternal. They are mythically known as the land of Lord Shiva. It is believed in Hinduism that he lives in these mountains and meditates in its secluded caves. Mount Kailash in Tibet is home to the lord of creation and destruction. At this moment, we are somewhere between Nepal and India. Maybe in both countries. There are no borders of barbed wire and steel here. A few kilometres from where we stand is the legendary temple of Pashupatinath in Nepal.'

As my journey commences towards Sandakphu, so do the legends. 'Madam, Hindu mythology speaks of a tale of Lord Shiva and the five Pandava brothers from the epic Mahabharata. After the fierce battle of Kurukshetra, the Pandavas had accumulated bad deeds by spilling the blood of their own brothers, the Kauravas. Riddled with pain and sorrow from the aftermath of the legendary war, the Pandavas decided to seek redemption in Shiva. They went looking for the lord of the Himalayas. Lord Shiva dodged and hid away from them. The chase went on till Shiva took the form of a big bull in disguise. The Pandavas recognized Shiva and began to chase the bull. Determined and desperate to seek redemption, the bull was flustered by the chase and dug his large head into the ground, only to be tugged at by the five brothers. The Pandavas caught its tail and compelled the bull to rise from the ground, taking his horns out of the mud; and the place where his head emerged is called Pashupatinath. It is considered to be one of the holiest places in our culture.'

Looking at the cobra lilies all around me, forming a path of flower snakes, and Lord Shiva in his meditative state, I drift into an alternate reality.

21

MAHAKAL, 'THE LAND OF TIME'

'Mahakal' is a version of Lord Shiva that depicts him as the 'Lord of Time'. Mahakal, in the Indian language Hindi, translates to 'the master of time'. Shiva is also the lord of all beginnings and endings. My father says, 'Time is a luxury that cannot be measured with wealth and once it passes, there is no going back. Time is continuous and infinite. It is the closest we humans have come to understanding God.'

At the very top of Darjeeling is the Mahakal Temple; there may be a vast number of temples dedicated to Lord Shiva in India, but the Himalayas remain Shiva's home. He is the most beloved deity among Hindu devotees. The Mahakal Temple in Darjeeling holds a unique significance. The serene mandir has a vibration like no other. At this very spot, both Buddhist and Hindu religions coexist. It is a place where the mantra '*Om Namah Shivaya*' meets '*Om Mani Padme Hum*'.

According to local history, before the town came into existence, there once lived a man called Dorjee. He was a spiritual practitioner and built his humble home at the very spot where this temple stands today. Being the first settler in these mountains, he made his mark on this land. Originally, there stood a single Buddhist monastery, one which is still used for worship by the Buddhist community today. The name Darjeeling was derived from this monk's name.

As I walk up the steep hill to the entrance of the temple,

I witness a large gathering of regular visitors—those other than humans. A large monkey population calls this temple their home and they surround me. I watch with amazement as they walk around the paved paths, dangle effortlessly from trees or wait impatiently on the corners of the roads, looking for humans to give them a snack. The sweet offerings to the temple are usually relished by these monkeys. I carry fruits and tamarind as offerings to the Gods in a small bowl covered with a napkin.

'Today is going to be a tug-of-war. One has to keep an eye out for these mischievous monkeys who tend to snatch fruits from your hands on the way up. I cannot reach empty-handed at the Mahakal Mandir. What will I say to the Gods? Blame it on the monkeys?'

I try to think of a solution while slowing my pace on the steep uphill climb. Some devotees carry bananas especially for them as it is their favourite snack.

I adopt this simple technique and begin distributing bananas to the monkeys on the way to the temple. I chant 'Om Namah Shivaya' while moving towards two mighty snow lions who stand guard at the top of the hill to welcome me into the temple. My hands are itching to ring the large iron bell to signal my arrival. Adorned with vibrant Tibetan prayer flags, the temple grounds give me a sense of peace and tranquillity, where two religions are connected with a single thread.

I finally enter the temple grounds. It is the time of 'sawan', i.e. during June–July, the month of Lord Shiva, when thousands of devotees, mostly Hindu priests or sadhus dressed in bright orange attire, come to pay their respects. Women flock to the temple of Shiva with devotion and a special request. Young women offer water to Lord Shiva, praying for a husband resembling him. Shiva and Parvati depict everlasting love, and they call out to young hearts in search of their other half. Devotees visit every day with vessels full of water, which is offered at the Shiva Lingam. Sadhus make this pilgrimage barefoot, chanting holy prayers on their journey up the mountains.

As I explore the temple further, the resident priest takes me on a tour of the secrets of the temple. 'Beyond the holy Shiva temple, there is a secret cave that only the priests know about.'

A middle-aged priest sits on the floor with his legs crossed and a bright red tika on his forehead, with a crimson shawl wrapped around him. 'I see you have come with a jar full of water. Shiva is known as "Bholenath"—one with a soft heart. He will certainly grant your wishes. Pour the water on the Shiva Lingam gently and add a few drops of milk to complete the ritual.'

Lost in the sandalwood scent floating in the air, I complete the ritual, after which the priest guides me forward. 'My child, let me glance at your future first,' Panditji says, taking my hand to read the lines of my destiny. He flips my left hand and begins to look at my palm. 'I see you have a long lifeline with a strong destiny. You have a clear palm with minimal crosses between the lines, signalling that your life will be a smooth one.' I gaze at my lifeline, stretching from the index finger to my wrist and ask, 'Panditji, what about my career and love line? What path will I choose?'

The priest takes a deep breath, focuses on the two tiny lines under my little finger and says, 'This is your affection line, which is coming out strong in your destiny. You will find love but you will find him somewhere far from here. Your career will bloom as you do.'

Suddenly, on a large rock where Panditji is seated, I visualize a boulder with an opening through which I can see the entrance to a narrow dark cave. The thought of going into this silent, slippery, cold cave is undoubtedly scary. Water drips in steady motion from the roof of the cave, and the pathway becomes narrower and narrower as I visualize entering the cave's mouth. It gives me a haunting sensation as I peep into its darkness. My voice gets lost inside it. I ask the resident priest whether it's even possible to go inside such a cave.

He calmly replies, 'Anything is possible, my child. Legend has it that this cave connects the Himalayas to the island nation of Lanka. We believe only the pure of heart—chanting the name of Shiva or Rama—can cross through without any harm. Ancient tales say one particular sadhu did go through this cave and happened to reach the tip of the border in southern India, near the Indian Ocean. Near Lanka.'

I find myself drawn to this legend as I have an adventurous soul. I further ask, 'Panditji, do you think this is the reason why there are so many monkeys in the Mahakal Mandir? Have they all arrived from Sri Lanka?'

He breaks into a peal of laughter, and his forehead crinkles. He says, 'You never know. Anything is possible in the land of Shiva. Monkeys are connected to the deity Hanuman, who has strong links to the Sri Lankan island. The famous epic Ramayana, where Hanuman played a key role in rescuing Goddess Sita, is a reminder of His glory. There is a temple dedicated to Lord Hanuman near the Shiva temple. You must pay it a visit before you leave the grounds.' The legend of Hanuman does not end there. According to belief, a large footprint of Lord Hanuman is imprinted in a rock here in Darjeeling. I have seen it for myself while strolling around its beautiful flower beds. Lord Hanuman, in the epic tale of Ramayana, came to the Himalayas in search of a magical herb called the 'sanjeevani booti' to save the injured Lakshmana,

Lord Rama's brother. On his travels, he set foot in Darjeeling and his footprints are still here to this day. The Himalayas are laden with herbs having miraculous healing abilities, which add to the mysticism of the land. It is believed that till the Mahakal Mandir stands, Darjeeling is protected and so are the people within.

22

MIRIK

The name 'Mirik' comes from the Lepcha word 'mir-yok', meaning 'a place burnt by fire'. The phrase *igne natura renovatur integra,* meaning 'through fire, nature is reborn whole', fits perfectly while describing the town of Mirik. It is located on the way to Darjeeling, situated in a misty mountain with large waterbodies. The main town is built around a large freshwater lake, which is usually covered with silvery mist drifting in from the surrounding forests. It's a magical sight as I sit on the wooden benches to gaze at the mist rolling in.

Mirik is a much-loved destination for the people of Darjeeling, especially when they need to escape the hustle of the busy town during the tourist season. The lake offers interesting vistas as one can watch colourful ducks, elegant swans, sleek fish, wild horses and exotic birds. The lake is also home to the rare Himalayan salamander, a creature previously thought to be extinct. The hidden lakes within the forest look tempting and call out to me to take a quick dip in, especially after my short and sweaty trek with the sun shining overhead. A few years earlier, we used to take a swim in these lakes, but now a signboard has been put up that says, 'Do not swim, Himalayan Salamander Conservation Lake. Do not disturb the natural habitat and breeding ground. This is a protected area.' This initiative has been taken by the region's forest department to increase the population of these rare amphibians.

Orange orchards and chamomile flowers grow freely in Mirik, and the rolling tea gardens accompany them. It is a delight for the body, mind and soul. Expansive tea gardens make me feel as if I am living a fairy tale. As I walk further, I come upon a little settlement in the middle of the valley—the Tabakoshi village. I watch my reflection in the transparent water while gazing at the boulders dotting the lakeside. This spot comes alive during the winter months as orange orchards transform winter's grey mood.

The highlight in Mirik for me has been the time we visited the fern stables; the town is known for its speciality in horse breeding, and this is where the story of Shadow and Spirit begins. We visited the stables before and picked out our two dashing stallions to be a part of the Oberoi clan. These charcoal black and chocolate brown beauties trotted into our lives from here.

Mirik is a place like no other; the elders of the village will narrate stories of its beginning as well as the local legends surrounding this land over a cup of hot Darjeeling tea. I have been visiting the lake often since I was a little girl with my parents. It makes for a perfect picnic spot and calls for a beautifully refreshing drive on the curved roads. The open forests are a delight, as there are small pathways that bring out the explorer in you.

I am sitting on a wooden bench on the forest trail when I see a lady who is gathering some firewood and dry twigs for her home. I notice her struggling, as she is also holding a bunch of belongings in her arms. I am sitting comfortably with nothing to do, so I think of lending her a helping hand. I walk up to her and offer my assistance if she is willing to accept it. She looks delighted and asks me to gather some dry wood and leaves scattered on the forest floor. While we are busy with the chores, having only each other for company in the woods, I begin a conversation with her and carry some dry twigs into her large 'doko' (a woven basket). This breaks the ice between us and she begins to ask me how I landed here and what my name is.

I smile softly and disclose my identity. 'Hello, my name is Rea.'

She reciprocates with an instant smile as we continue our little conversation. 'You do not live in Mirik, do you? I have not seen you around and trust me, I have been around for a long time.' The stranger seems wise from her appearance.

'I am from Darjeeling, but I wouldn't say that I am not from around here. Mountains are where I am from,' I say and keep the momentum going.

The stranger taps my back gently and says, 'You seem clever for your age. I wonder if you are interested to know some local tales of Mirik to keep us company while we pick pieces of wood.'

Maybe it is her way of thanking me. This is what I have been waiting for. I am eager to listen to the local legends of Mirik.

As this stranger walks next to me, she starts speaking in the local language, which I am fluent in. As I live in Darjeeling, speaking the local tongue comes naturally, no matter what one's ethnic background may be. One by one, she picks up some scattered branches from the uneven soil and says softly, 'Mirik is secretly known as the land of snakes. Before mankind inhabited this land, Mirik was said to be home to the Naga Kingdom. These beings were part man and part snake and they had the ability to shapeshift.

'This community lived and thrived in these woodlands. They were a very peaceful race who worked with the magic of the land to create a thriving and sustainable society. The soil in this region is still known for its highly fertile nature. Legend has it that the Naga King and Queen had their palaces made of natural minerals in these dense forests. Sadly, as time passed, a cloud of misfortune came over this community. A devastating forest fire triggered by heavy lightning strikes engulfed the entire forest, taking the Naga community with it, and driving the rest of them far from this land. Their flourishing race was wiped out in this region because of this catastrophic event.'

The stranger's story tugs at my heartstrings. She continues her tale, 'The Naga King and Queen were believed to have a magical blue diamond in their possession, which is known to mankind as the "nagamani". The diamond is the size of two fists put together. An extraordinary gem! This priceless jewel was lost in the fury of the fire, engulfed by the roaring landmass. Legend has it that this jewel is lying deep within the layers of the mountains, and this is what makes the soil so enriched. The land is blessed by the presence of this magical jewel and therefore, the people of Mirik hold snakes in high regard. Hindus consider the snake as a deity. We pray to the snake coiled on the neck of the Hindu God of destruction, Lord Shiva. In India, snakes are revered as a sign of prosperity, wisdom and enlightenment.'

Sharing her tale, the wise woman invites me into her little cottage for some delicious chamomile tea that she grows in her backyard. My thoughts float into the mythical world of the Nagas with every whistle on the kettle luring me in. Delicate chamomile warms my cold lips while I am sitting in the cottage of a stranger, somewhere deep in the woods of Mirik.

23

THE SACRED PLANT

Living among tea planters, I hear mysteries of this sacred plant at our Himalayan home. My father sips on the first flush of Darjeeling's superstar, our freshly picked organic tea. His dear friend, Mr Raja, arrives from the gardens to enjoy our much-beloved custom of high tea. Cutting the edge of his cigar with a pair of scissors, holding a napkin in hand, he prepares to blow smoke into the cold air as he lights up his Cuban. Taking off a maroon silk scarf from around his neck, Mr Raja speaks to us in his deep voice.

'My dear, let me tell you our side of the story. We planters have a strong connection to this land. The first tea plant was brought into Darjeeling about 150 years ago from China by the British during their occupation of our country. They planted and cultivated it in these high mountains. The first tea seeds (*Camellia sinensis*) were brought as an experiment to Darjeeling. Soon after its success, our tea gardens grew to be world-famous, holding the title of the best tea in the world. Darjeeling tea is proudly called "the champagne of tea" and we are its proud cultivators. What a blessing it is to be the caretaker of such a sacred plant. Let me tell you where the real magic lies. Our land not only looks different from the rest of the Himalayan belt, but the tea cultivated here smells and tastes different too. This is our identity!'

My father, listening to his words, adds a bit of his own

flavour to the brew. 'Raja is most definitely on to a good point here. Tea is not just a liquid but a sacred natural potion. According to local legend, a poor farmer, during the reign of Emperor Qianlong in China, came across an old dilapidated temple whose deity was a Buddhist bodhisattva named Guanyin. This female deity was the Goddess of Mercy, revered since ancient times. The poor farmer had the urge to clear the temple of its wild encroachment and began to plan his next move. Without the means to restore the temple, the poor farmer wanted to do something about its decaying condition so he started with a simple idea. He took a broomstick and began cleaning the temple grounds slowly as he visited the farmlands nearby. Days went by, and soon the temple was beginning to look alive again. With a pure heart, he lit an incense at the shrine as he continued with his daily life. His devotion and selfless intentions spoke volumes about his unshakeable patience. As the clock turned its hands, this kind-hearted farmer had a dream about the Goddess of Mercy.

'The day had arrived when the bodhisattva disclosed a very important message to the farmer and directed him to an old cave located behind the temple. The Goddess of Mercy said to him that there was hidden treasure inside it. Because his actions were directed by his pure heart, a gift was waiting for him inside the secret cave. She directed him to make good use of this gift and asked him to share it with the rest of humanity. So the farmer promptly followed the bodhisattva's direction and reached the cave, which he had failed to notice in his previous visits. He went inside the cave, and to his wonder, discovered the treasure—it was a single tea shoot growing in the otherwise desolate cave. He thanked Goddess Guanyin for his vision and took the tea root home to grow and nurture it. As the shoot bloomed into a beautiful large bush, he tasted the delicate leaves and brewed them. To his amazement, it was unlike any other plant he had ever come across. As per the instructions he had received, the kind farmer shared this treasure with his entire village and asked them to nurture it and spread it in the entire province. He gave it the name "Tieguanyin" aka "The Iron Goddess". This sacred plant spread throughout his village and the province into China.

'This tree is a national treasure to this day and the legendary tea bush still exists in China; the kind farmer's name is carved on a hill near the original tea plant. My love for history made me initiate the legacy of tea to be carried out as a tradition in The Elgin's Duchess Lounge. This is why I hold the high tea ritual in high regard. We celebrate this magical herb by indulging our guests with a special afternoon tea menu. I am very particular about my tea. You know that, don't you? A selection of fresh Darjeeling black teas, Earl Grey, fresh lemon, herbal, chamomile, jasmine, green tea and Indian masala tea (or chai) served with a wide range of cakes, cookies, shortbread and scones from our bakery. They are my weak spot.'

I pick up a butter scone and, taking a big bite, say, 'Yes, Papa, I do know you have a strong sweet tooth. It might have rubbed off only a little bit on me. But it surely caught hold of Aanyaa.'

My father takes a sip of his sacred drink and says, 'I am not done yet, Rea! There is more to this brew; high tea is a ritual at The Elgin. The beginning of the tradition takes us back in time to the 1800s when an evening snack was introduced in the chambers of the Belvoir Castle by Duchess Anna Maria Stanhope of Bedford, who is credited with creating the world-renowned afternoon ritual. This became very popular among the aristocrats and it was picked up by the rest of Europe.

This much-loved afternoon tea tradition is a speciality at The Elgin. I am a man of tradition and I thrive by keeping it alive within my walls.'

Our mountains have a divine feminine shakti; I feel the love of a mother, the caress of a grandmother and the embrace of a spirit. Among the green tea leaves grows white nectar; the white tea is legendary for its unmatched quality, luxurious essence and medicinal purposes in the Asian subcontinent. Its origin is surrounded by myth and legend, making it 'The Maharaja' of the tea world.

∽

The month of June is here. Heavy monsoon showers have turned into a drizzle. The sky seems to be in quite the mood. It's a misty cold day as the sun is hiding behind the clouds. I am relaxing on the Persian carpet by the window of The Elgin lobby. It seems like Lord Indra is playing with his sceptre, about to shower water all over us at any moment. I glance at two hotel guests who are battling it out on the marble chessboard, and it seems intense. *A match is surely fun to watch when the opponents are challenging enough and this seems to be a tough one*, I think to myself. While they were busy with the game, I was more interested in their conversation. Every day is a new learning experience. Travellers come to the hotel with a lot more than their heavily packed suitcases. This young couple start narrating a tale that draws me even closer to Darjeeling's roots.

The young man, clad entirely in black, suddenly says, 'Checkmate! My white horse yet again takes me to victory.'

He is pouring piping hot white tea into his fine china. 'Well, my dear, this tea is absolutely refreshing! You must try some. Do you know why white tea is known as the "white enchantress" in these mountains? Let me spin the wheel of time while you play your next move. Legend has it that in the foothills of Mount Taishan in China, the white tea bush was first discovered. It displayed a dissimilar figure to the widely found green-leaved bushes in the province. The white tea bush has fine silvery-white hairs on the unopened buds. This unique quality sets it apart from the rest of the tea family. I was surprised to know that during an epidemic in that province of China, the white tea bush was used to help cure the affected people. Ever since that day, the white tea plant is well known for its healing properties. Isn't that amazing? This is the reason why white tea is a luxury and draws people to its silvery strands. Its faint aroma is captivating and it is very light on the stomach. I feel refreshed and energized enough to make my next move on the chessboard.

'Beware, my dear, for I have just had Himalayan nectar. I have ventured into these Himalayas especially to enjoy the first flush directly from these tea gardens. The first flush of white tea is sold worldwide in a niche market and it is given the title "The King of Tea". Rare extracts of the white tea plant are used in many modern-day medications, which prove highly beneficial for the human body.'

The young European couple notices me in the corner and can sense my inclination towards their conversation, so they invite me to join them for their next chess match. We quickly acquaint ourselves. During our conversation, they too are drawn towards an alluring energy coming from my necklace. The lady asks, 'Darling, what is this sitting beautifully on your neck?'

I hold my gemstone, which is a princess-cut garnet dangling on a gold cross. Its striking colour always captures the attention of jewellery lovers.

'I wear this garnet near my heart to soothe my heart chakra and align my vibrations. It also helps me channel my energy,' I tell the couple who are still battling it out on the chessboard.

'Here! Would you like to have a closer look at it?' I take off my necklace and place it in the hands of the foreigner. The ancient Indian culture of working with natural gemstones for chakra healing and productivity awes this couple. As the night goes on, I thank them for the wonderful tale they shared with me. Although I live in the land of tea, this particular legend was surprisingly unheard of. No one spoke about the origins of the white tea plant, but these travellers had brought something new to the table.

My parents are out of town for the whole week, so I extend an invitation for dinner to the couple, which they happily accept. Being a good host is in my blood, and I surely know how to cheer up The Elgin guests. I offer them our speciality drink, called 'Green Elgin', which is a blend of mint syrup, pineapple juice and fresh cucumber, with Sprite on top. I also offer them a complimentary stress relieving massage at the Snow Spa. It is the least I could do in return for the wonderful knowledge I received from them.

24

MANDALA

As the night creeps in and the stars come out to say hello, The Elgin too lights up, along with our in-house modes of entertainment. Apart from movie nights, a variety of board games, chakra healing sessions, auric colour therapy, aroma therapy, sunset photography in the courtyard and star gazing are on the agenda. The healing sessions and outdoor activities particularly call out to me.

Aanyaa and I have planned something for tonight. With all the aura therapy rooms booked and the chakra healers occupied, I make my way towards the second-best thing. The gaming section. I choose to indulge in a game of Ludo with my friends who are visiting us for a sleepover. It's always a good idea to have company while the night is still young. I opt for a large Persian cushion with my legs crossed, ready to try my luck. While playing the game of Ludo, my mind suddenly drifts towards a parallel realm. Within a minute, the surroundings disappear into a cloudy haze while the various voices vanish into thin air, but my attention is on the square board lying on the marble tabletop. Its hypnotic layout— divided into four columns, each of a different colour—takes me into the mystic realm of mandalas. I could hear Jethi's voice guiding my subconscious mind.

'Mandalas are the sacred geometry of the Brahmanda, the universe, which is known to have a sacred code to decipher its mystery. It is also called the "sacred language of the cosmos". These languages are in the form of geometry, colours, sounds, numbers and beyond. The Buddhist monks describe this layout beautifully in the form of sacred mandalas. Monks create these codes by means of artwork in their paintings, scriptures, sculptures and thankas. Most of these descriptions are found in hand-painted thankas, depicting the different realms of the afterlife, cosmic astronomy and the realm of the spirit world. Certain mandalas depict the abode of heavenly beings and the creation of the universe in detail. Each one is a masterpiece on its own, intricately hand-painted and carefully weaved over time by meditating craftsmen, who use pure gold threads to weave the designs, which makes each piece unique and rare to find.' Jethi's words awaken my subconscious.

As I am lost in a conversation with myself, something suddenly flashes in my mind. I recall a moment when I was walking slowly in a monastery where an old lama was chanting with his prayer beads. Clad entirely in orange, the lama had transported my young mind to a land of ancient cosmic geometry. With a wrinkled face and calm green eyes, he said to me, 'Hear me, child, the word "mandala" comes from the Sanskrit word "mandal", meaning a circle. Mandalas are used in Hinduism, Buddhism, Jainism and Shintoism as a tool for meditation and ascension. It helps one reach a meditative state with ease. Like a compass for a sailor, the figurations of different patterns on the mandala serve as a guiding tool used to create a sacred space to focus your energies in one fixed direction. A human being's energy flow is usually scattered in multiple directions; mandalas help you focus and align that scattered energy towards one's spiritual growth. In Eastern cultures, mandalas depict a pathway to a sacred space, depicting the cosmic alignment, astral spaces, the map of various paradises and abode of heavenly beings, and it continues to spread into multiple branches like that of a sacred banyan tree. In some cases, mandalas also depict the journey of the soul through different realms of the afterlife and the underworld. Some also describe the various stages in the Buddha's life. It is a means of imparting knowledge and focus or dhyana to access the different spiritual planes of the cosmic ocean. It is a diagram that connects the universe with the minds and hearts of humanity.'

I basked in his wisdom as I walked through the monastery's grounds, decorated with sacred ancient mandalas. I had drifted into deep thought when a faint voice from reality jolts me to the present.

'Rea, it's your turn to roll the dice. Let's not break the flow of the game. I am almost home,' Aanyaa says, while I shake myself back to reality.

'Here. Six!' I say out loud. I look at my sister and murmur, 'Hey, doesn't this board feel like a mandala? We are rolling our destiny numbers onto its colours.'

Aanyaa, sipping on her chamomile tea, addresses all of us. 'You may have a point here. It does remind me of sacred geometry. I am glad you sensed it, Rea. Now I am free to share this profound knowledge with you. So listen up. These sacred mandalas provide a deeper meaning to the understanding of the workings of the universe and the evolution of the human being with the structure of life itself. At almost every Tibetan Buddhist monastery in the Himalayas, I have come across different types of mandalas, all of which depict various aspects of the universe or the universe by itself. It teaches us oneness and collective consciousness. The monks create mandalas with beautiful vibrant colours and fresh flowers, weaving them with golden thread and most commonly through visual paintings. One of my personal favourites is the depiction of the universe on the mandala with Mount Meru at the centre of the universe, surrounded by the various astral continents and oceans on all sides. According to Tibetan Buddhism, they created a sacred space centuries ago to impart teaching in the form of beautiful diagrams and depictions. Followers get a deeper understanding of the cosmic structure through artwork instead of reading it via various texts and scriptures. Mandalas were the simplest way of communicating this to people in the olden times. On my many visits to the monastery, I always ask the resident monks to explain the meaning of different mandalas that are present on their grounds. With each visit, I absorb something new about the sacred configuration of the universal code. My voyage into the ocean of knowledge seems closer to its destination. Just a little closer.'

Lost in the realm of mandalas, I suddenly grab Aanyaa's hand and blink twice in quick succession, signalling to her telepathically, *The time has come. Venus is perfectly aligned with the new moon tonight. Let's go, Aanyaa. It's time for a reading!*

We move into our sacred space quietly. The mellow wind chimes in the attic ring in the breeze as the sheer curtains billow. Aanyaa cleanses the air with sage while chanting her 'Devi mantra' out loud. *Om Tara, Om Tara! I summon the divine Goddess Tara.* Aanyaa sits on the floor with her legs crossed under the new moon's light. She gathers her energy and lays her hands on a secret symbol.

Dressed in a white lace gown, wearing silver bangles on both hands, I watch her glow. The Himalayan high priestess is in her sacred space tonight. Aanyaa looks ethereal as she locks her hazel eyes onto mine and says, 'Rea, gather up your energies before you hold my yogini tarot deck in your hands.

Breathe in and out a couple of times, totally easing your energy flow. Relax your mind... Relax... Now think of what you are looking for. Put your focus on one specific question.'

I close my eyes, taking a moment to myself. I take a bowl carved out of a dry coconut shell with a colourful mandala design on it—a lotus encircled by loops of vibrant patterns, which holds an amethyst. I pick up the amethyst and focus its energy on my crown chakra. I then gently place the amethyst crystal on my head. 'Aanyaa, I am focused now. Let the yoginis give their prophecy tonight.'

Aanyaa pulls out her yogini tarot deck and says, 'Rea, let me begin with the three-card reading. I sense an urge to do this spread for you. Let's see what is hidden from us and what is coming for us under the new moon's light.' Aanyaa takes out a bundle of navy blue cards and places a rose quartz over it. She then sprinkles fresh rose water on the heart-shaped quartz while chanting her mantra. *'Om... Om Yogini! Om Yogini!'* She invokes the sacred yoginis. 'Rea, watch as I align the natural elements. Rose quartz helps with healing the heart chakra and cleanses past traumas. It is my personal favourite out of the crystal family. Energy reading is all about vibrations. My actions cleanse the energy of the room and bring an angelic presence around us. Connect with your archangels and ask them to guide you through this reading. Connect to Goddess Tara and the mystical yoginis.'

I pause for a moment to soak it all in.

'When you are ready, touch this yogini deck with your right hand and connect to the tarot cards,' she says while touching her little finger to her index. 'The time is right, Rea. The light of the new moon is shining directly on the cards. It is a good moment to begin our reading. Now place your right hand on the cards.' I gently put my hand under the new moon's light, a moonstone glimmering on my ring finger. Connected with it, I ask a question.

'Lunar Goddess, please light my path and show me what is hidden; what lies in my destiny?'

I open my eyes to see Aanyaa shuffling the energized tarot cards, and then dividing them into three equal piles. She gently places one card over the other till they're on the same level.

'Rea, pick one pile. Just go with the flow.'

My hand reaches for the middle pile and I have chosen.

'All right then!' Aanyaa says as she puts together all three piles and spreads them on the wooden table in the shape of a fan. 'Now pick three cards from the tarot spread. Let your intuition guide you. Gently pick any three that you are drawn to, Rea,' Aanyaa says while humming her chant. I stretch my hand to pick out three cards when suddenly one card moves as a gust of cold wind through the open window displaces it from the tarot spread. Aanyaa quickly pauses and turns her face towards the Moon. 'This is a sign, Rea. This particular card has been chosen by your angels. So now, pick two cards from the spread. Seems like one has already been picked out for you.'

I gather my energies, pick two cards and wait for the oracle to decipher its mystery. Aanyaa takes the three tarot cards from the deck and gently turns them around to reveal my prophecy. 'My darling sister, this three-card reading symbolizes your past, present and future. I feel a strong angelic presence here right now. Let me uncover what our angels want us to know.'

Aanyaa flips the tarot cards to glance at my future. The first card is The High Priestess, the second is The Six of Swords and the third is The Lovers. Aanyaa clears her throat and says, 'Hmm... This is interesting. Very interesting indeed! I see your past is full of spiritual development brought on by The High

Priestess; you have been summoned to your divine path. This explains why you behave like an old lady at times.' Aanyaa lightens the mood before continuing, 'I see The Six of Swords in your present. You are going through some sort of emotional turmoil, which is making you feel trapped. Look closely at the card, at this image of a lady blindfolded with six swords in her hand. Almost like she is fighting a battle she cannot see. I sense you are going through an emotional rollercoaster with someone causing you immense pain.' I listen silently to what my oracle sister has to say. 'Rea, now we come to the future! Your future has The Lovers' card.'

I heave a sigh of relief. 'The Lovers' card is a positive sign for love in the future. This card signals your soulmate's arrival.' Aanyaa's hazel eyes glitter as she gives me the good news. 'Don't worry, Rea, these dark clouds will soon pass and you will be in your lover's arms.' Aanyaa and I gaze at the moon as I await my soulmate's arrival.

25

THE FOREST AND THE NYMPH

Before the tea gardens came into existence in Darjeeling, the Himalayan mountains were brimming with undisturbed coniferous and oak forests. Some of the tales from those times have been passed down the generations as folklore in the mountains.

Our forest is worshipped and revered by its Himalayan caretakers. These enchanted forests are our protectors, guides, means of existence and the cradle of our life. These hair-raising stories are narrated by my classmate's ninety-year-old grandmother, who is one of the first members of our community. She sheds light on Darjeeling's tales that are believed to be true. I let the wind guide me as I visit my friend's house in Bhutia Busty. I have come to indulge in secret stories of the land while sipping on a hot cup of chamomile tea, perched in her courtyard beside a tiny fire.

The old lady, wrapped up in a blanket, says, 'I want to impart some knowledge of the forest around us to you children before it dies out with my generation. So listen carefully, girls! In ancient times, the open forests were a place of enchantment. A womb brimming with life! Now, the increasing population in the hills have driven away many supernatural beings that used to call these forests their home. With excessive human activity, there is no space for any other creature to thrive. We can see it happening even with the wild animals of our forest today. Animals go into hiding and move deeper and deeper, away from the human population, to live peacefully. A similar thing has happened with the supernatural beings of the forest. If mankind would discover them, it would only create destruction of their race and drive them to extinction.'

She begins to narrate a true story. The old lady's grandmother witnessed it herself while living in a small hut in Darjeeling. This was when this old lady's grandmother was a little girl of about six or seven. She was collecting firewood in the forest for her house. They used firewood for cooking and to keep their homes warm at night. It was a daily routine, but one day, the girl wandered off a little from the usual track and reached deep into the forest. People usually headed home in those days before nightfall because the forest is a dangerous place to wander in at night. Many people have lost their way in the dark woods as each pathway appears to be the same, vanishing into the forest's umbra with no sunlight illuminating the way back home. As the girl realized what time it was, she quickly gathered all her belongings, put them into her doko (her woven carry bag) and started to walk home. She began to sing so as to entertain herself on the lonely walk home when she was distracted by a bright flashing light. The light was so strong that it was almost blinding. The little girl could feel the presence of something supernatural blocking her path.

'Her skin grew pale and a chill went down her spine. Her tiny legs froze on the ground as she looked at the path before her. This mysterious being appeared to be taller than the trees itself, emitting a royal blue light, nearly dazzling her.

'With her feet frozen on the ground, she stood in front of this mysterious being, who asked her to go back home in peace. When she asked the supernatural form, "What are you?" she got no answer in return. Instead, it asked her a question.

"I will grant you one wish. Just one! Tell me, what do you desire the most in this world?" The little girl, with her eyes firmly covered, looked down at her feet and asked the entity, "I wish to be married one day to the most handsome and wealthy man in the land." The deep voice echoed through the forest and said, "Your wish is granted."

'All of a sudden, the bright light disappeared into the depths of the forest. The little girl was stunned by her supernatural encounter and she let her survival instinct take hold and ran back home as quickly as she could. She hurried to her mother and narrated the entire story, flabbergasted and amazed by what she had just encountered in the deep forest. Her mother hugged her and said that she had just come in contact with a supernatural spirit of the forest, known as the genie. The wish-fulfilling genie had granted the little girl's deepest desire. As time passed and the little girl grew to be an elegant woman, she was married to one of the village chief's handsome sons who had a deep fondness for her. It was a marriage of love! So her wish had been fulfilled, and this tale has become a part of our heritage.

∽

On a bright colourful autumn day, the oak and maple trees look stunning, clad in orange and amber hues. Energetic squirrels are out playing in the Duchess Garden. I can hear them from my window. I feel like a nymph in the forest, sitting with my legs crossed on the white swing behind the gazebo. I am relishing our signature drink, The Elgin's Beauty Queen. This cocktail, made with a few drops of honey, has been specially created in honour of my mother by our skilled bartenders. This was gifted to my mother on her birthday by The Elgin family. The Elgin's Beauty Queen is a blend of fresh fruits with vodka and some Cointreau on top. It is similar to a wine float and yet feels like its distant cousin. It is my mother's favourite and is one of the most refreshing drinks on the menu.

Wrapped in a pashmina shawl, I see the fish pond in my direct line of sight. I observe dainty goldfish creating bubbles on the water's surface when my mother's dear friend Pema walks in through the gates for a routine chat.

I greet her with a warm hug and offer her some snacks to binge on. She has recently returned from a camping trip near the Teesta River. During her trip in the nearby forest expanse, she came across a Himalayan legend, narrated to her by one of the local guides. She was overjoyed to share it with me as it revolves around our hometown.

With a plate of sumptuous scones, Scottish delights and chocolate brownies, Pema begins, 'Long ago, when the wild forest overshadowed the human settlements, there was once a young man who belonged to a local tribe. He went out into the forest for a routine hunt. He was well-known throughout the land for his hunting skills. Once a week, he would wander deep into the woods to hunt. He was extremely pompous and arrogant as he had mastered the bow and arrow. He would always come back victorious, and he would boast about having conquered the forest. "I am the ruler of this forest." The egoistic man would say this out loud while entering the village grounds. He brought back squirrels, bears, deer and any other animal that would dare to cross his path. The hunter had the ego of a mountain.

'Year after year, he'd go on his mission of conquest and return to the small village, which comprised of a cluster of huts. One cold night, the pompous man went out on his routine hunt and set up many animal traps. This was the "huntsman's language" he was well-versed with. He was a lone ranger, brilliant when it came to navigating the uncharted forest. The young man set up a skilled trap with shaved wood, ropes and sharp metal edges. He covered it up with large green leaves and waited… Time kept ticking and the hours went by with him in hiding, seated on a treetop beside the trap he had built.

'The hours felt unusually long this time. As a result of his long wait, he fell asleep. The sun was about to set when the hunter was woken by a sudden noise in the grass below. He was startled to see a beautiful spotted deer, unlike any he had come across in these forests. The hunter had his eyes on the prize. The spotted deer was wandering about the forest, ignorant of the presence of danger lurking on the treetop. The hunter waited for a while till he ran out of patience. The sun had begun to set and he started tracking its movement. The deer had somehow managed to avoid the trap. The young hunter followed quietly. He found a perfect moment and stretched his bow while taking aim at his target. The hunter shot an arrow while creeping in from behind the deer when suddenly, a small noise startled the deer.

'The arrow hit the deer's leg instead of its back. A loud cry was heard throughout the forest and all the birds on the treetops took flight. The deer was in agony. Within a few minutes, it was pitch-black. The hunter went towards the injured deer thinking to himself about how proud he was of getting his aim even in minimal light.

'The hunter moved towards the injured deer. When he stepped forward, he was startled. It shocked him as he witnessed something unreal. It was a full moon night. The rays of the moon landed on the deer, who had transformed into a beautiful woman. It was magic. The hunter's hands were shaking with the weapons he held in his tight grip. The deer was a shapeshifter. For the first time in his life, his heart was filled with guilt. His body trembled, his pupils dilated and a sense of fear, uncertainty and wonderment filled him. The hunter contemplated his next steps and walked towards the beautiful shapeshifter. He removed his sharp arrow, which had pierced her thigh. The shapeshifter let him approach her as she was in unbearable pain. He tended to her wounds and gave her shelter in his tent for the night.

'The hunter was startled by what he had just witnessed as he sat by the bonfire with her, looking up at the heavens with the full moon shining overhead. He noticed the moon had a blue halo around it that night. Something he had never seen before. The hunter put his head on a bunch of hay near the warm fire and fell asleep. When he woke, he discovered the forest nymph had disappeared into the wild in the early hours of the morning, never to be seen again. That night, the deer had turned into a beautiful woman, but it was not the only thing that magically transformed. The hunter transformed with her. *Natura nihil frustra facit* (nature does nothing in vain). The skilled and pompous hunter never went out to kill any animals again. His arrogance washed away with the ripples of the river he had camped beside. He was transformed by what he had witnessed, just like the transformation of the forest nymph.'

26

THE GLAMOROUS MEMSAHIB

On a busy day at The Elgin, I open my bedroom door to venture out for a lunch invitation to the Duke Hall when I overhear a group of housekeepers gossiping amongst themselves about a topic that is of interest to me. We have some special guests amidst us this week. We are hosting a few film stars. The hotel is filled with excitement and everyone, from the chefs to the front office manager, is literally star-struck. Suddenly, the bellboys are in spotless uniforms. Housekeepers are overjoyed to be up close and personal with the stars at The Elgin. The gossip revolves around the actresses and, to my surprise, the main focus of their conversation swiftly shifts to the 'glamorous memsahib'.

The words 'glamorous memsahib' catch my attention because I know that the 'memsahib' of The Elgin is no one else but my mother. The Elgin has been hosting many actresses from the Indian film industry lately. The housekeeping department is especially thrilled by their glittering presence. I stand there, eavesdropping on the housekeepers.

'Our Memsahib is the most elegant lady. Nimmi Memsahib carries herself gracefully, whether it is a traditional saree or a modern business suit. Have you noticed her style statement?' Then the other housekeeper says, 'Her black business suit is my favourite. She is certainly more glamorous than any of the actresses. Nimmi Memsahib is a natural beauty.'

A third housekeeper comes out of the bathroom with a broom, saying, 'When we enter her suite to serve her breakfast in the early morning hours, her face looks radiant. While actresses have glowing skin, theirs is artistically textured, whereas our Memsahib glows from within. She washes her face with rice water every morning, following a simple skincare routine. I have watched her apply a transparent lip balm that brings out her natural lip colour.'

It is hard to hide anything from our housekeepers. In the corner, I see my housekeeper, Chanda, rolling out the carpet and saying, 'It's true. Nimmi Memsahib is perfect in every aspect. The best thing about her is that she does not let her clothing and jewellery outshine her natural charm. She is not arrogant, even though she is the lady of the house. Nimmi Memsahib always greets us with love and respect. I cannot recall even a single moment when our Memsahib addressed us in a loud or rude tone. Her face always has a glowing smile that can uplift one's mood even on the most stressful of days. We are so blessed to have her as our boss. I remember a time, not so long ago, when she was empathetic towards me when I lost my father. She has been a pillar of strength in my dark days, which is something I will never forget. Diamond Sir and Nimmi Memsahib make such a wonderful pair. Both complement each other.'

On hearing such wonderful things about my parents, I remember that they strongly believe in—*Sic parvis magna* (greatness from small beginnings), and they have surely lived up to it.

I observe everything and everyone, waiting silently for the housekeepers to finish their chores. They clean the bedroom, and I quietly push the door so that I can pass by unnoticed. Heading down to the Duke Hall, I have a smile on my face as their words swirl through my mind.

I join my parents for lunch, seated on a circular table decorated with red candle stands. Avocado salad dressed with cottage cheese and fresh tomato soup is waiting for me.

'I am sorry, Papa. I was delayed due to a conversation that captured my attention in the corridors.' I glance over the table at my mother's hazel eyes as she seems to enjoy her soup.

'Rea, your soup is getting cold. Please don't keep your food waiting. These avocados have come from Sikkim this morning. Home-grown and completely organic,' my mother says, pulling up a chair for me next to her. I notice Mama wearing blue sapphires on her wrist, which immediately catches my attention.

'Mama, I have a quick question,' I say, my eyes on the sapphires. 'Where did you get this? May I borrow it for a few days? It will fit me perfectly because we are the same size.' I wink at her.

'Well, my darling, Diamond bought this blue bracelet for me on our trip to Sri Lanka. The island nation is known for its sapphires. It was a twinkling surprise for me. I have an entire jewellery set with it. A choker necklace and chandelier earrings. Oh, that reminds me, I have given a sapphire ring to Aanyaa.'

I hold my mother's hand and say, 'I want one too.'

'Well, my dear, sapphires are mysterious stones. Specifically blue sapphires. These gems should not be taken lightly. It is called "neelam" in India due to its deep blue colour. I asked Aanyaa to wear the neelam on her middle finger to boost her energy. Like most mysterious things, there is a catch to it. The neelam has a notorious reputation for being very picky when it comes to its wearer. It does not suit everyone. Sapphire or "Santi Priya" in Sanskrit is a special gemstone, connected to

Vedic astrology and sciences. Dear to Saturn, the neelam is a very powerful jewel that can prove exceedingly beneficial or totally tragic for the person wearing it. Especially a large carat. You must conduct a test before wearing my neelam bracelet. Are you ready for it?' my mother says, sprinkling some salt and pepper into her bowl of soup.

'Definitely! I am ready for the test. What do I need to do for the sapphire's approval?'

'Rea, take the bracelet and put it under your pillow at night before you go to bed. Observe your dream when you wake up, think about it over breakfast and sense how you feel. Heavy or light? Did you have a pleasant dream or a confusing one? Once you have done this, then you can wear this bracelet. Why don't you try it tonight? While we were in Sri Lanka, your father was lured into buying blue sapphires for me. The most photographed person in the world, Princess Diana, wore an engagement ring crafted with this mysterious blue sapphire. An 18-carat stone.

'A jeweller in Sri Lanka was dazzled by your father and said, "Sir, is your name Mr Diamond? Well, you have walked into the right place. Only a diamond can cut through a blue sapphire."'

'Okay mama, I have another question. You gave me my name, while Papa named Viraj and Aanyaa. Why is that?'

'My last child had to be named by me. I made up my mind and decided to give you a short and sweet name. I stumbled upon the name "Rhea", and decided to change the spelling to "Rea" when you were born. Rhea is an ancient Roman Goddess, a powerful titan and the wife of Cronus. Blue sapphires may just suit you as Cronus is another name for Saturn. Rhea is one of Saturn's largest moons. Saturn may be accepting of you wearing sapphires.'

'Well, I'm glad you named me Rea! I cannot imagine being called anything else. Suits me perfectly, Mama,' I say with a large smile.

'Yes, I'm glad I did or your Papa would have named you "Ruby" instead!' My mother puts her spoon down on the table as we all laugh our way out of the luncheon.

'Ruby? Then we would certainly be a "gem" of a family.'

I follow the queen of the castle into the Duchess Garden where she is wrapping a soft shawl around herself and settling down under a blossoming tree. 'My dear, this tree is my beloved. I had one like this growing up opposite my house when I was young. I have spent many days and nights under her shadow. Her red flowers take me back to my childhood.' My mother is sitting under the flame of the forest.

'Rea, tomorrow is a special night. The stars have something in store for us. It is a total lunar eclipse tomorrow. I want you and Aanyaa to clearly follow my instructions. This is a cleansing ritual passed down to me by my mother. A time to focus our feminine energies.' My mother takes me into the lands of my ancestors. 'You girls must follow the cleansing ritual tomorrow by fasting all day till the eclipse is over. It's a matter of twenty-four hours without food or water. Only then can we commence the lunar ritual.'

Agreeing to her terms and conditions, I have a sumptuous dinner and go to bed. The next day, Aanyaa and I are ready for the full moon rituals.

My mother holds a copper coin, standing near the holy tulsi growing on the balcony of her room. It is getting darker, the night is setting in with the arrival of the eclipse. She asks us to follow her every move. Then, as the moon is engulfed in the sky, she takes the coin and buries it in the soil. It is dark and quiet. She takes a glass of water and pours it gently on the holy tulsi plant as the moon shows us her face again. We follow all rituals.

I gaze into her hazel eyes and my father's words ring in the air. *Tum omnibus una omnis subripuit Veneres* (for she has stolen all the charms of Venus from everyone together).

27

THE CALLING

It is a warm Friday afternoon, and mist clings to the stone walls of Loreto Convent. Just like most of the infrastructure in Darjeeling, the convent's walls are full of history.

An old chapel stands strong and steady at the entrance of the convent. I have spent most of my time under her evergreen trees, growing up alongside the incredible Irish nuns and their unshakeable faith in the Almighty. Living with them, hearing their stories and learning from them have shaped me into the person I am today.

These old stones talk to me, these wise trees know my name and the large classroom still echoes with the sounds of our mischief, thereby creating a home away from home. At times, when I want to run away from the world, these grounds protect and comfort me. Within these walls, I come across a beautiful tale about a calling.

The Irish nuns all speak about their initiation into the convent. Each story is unique. Their personal journeys from a land far away to this present moment amidst the mountains.

'Home is an expression, a feeling,' the Irish nuns said fondly. The convent, in the high Himalayas, far away from the oceans of Ireland, has become their new home. 'My dear, there is something magical about this place.' The nuns have travelled far and wide to spread their beliefs until they stopped their journey right at this spot.

What is it that makes them stop and call this place their home? This question always rings in my mind.

The nuns always smile and say, 'It is a calling, my dear! The Almighty guided us to these sacred mountains.'

The relationship between the Almighty and the nuns is sacrosanct. The nuns dedicate their entire life to the cause of helping the unfortunate, poor and needy. Their mission is astounding. Sister Teresa, one of the nuns in the convent, takes us on a journey of spiritual awakening over a cup of hot tea.

The people of Darjeeling take their teatime very seriously. Even here at the convent. Almost everywhere in town, the long conversations always begin with a cup and end with one too.

After clearing her throat, Sister Teresa says in a calm but stern manner, 'My dears, this is the land of the rising sun. The northeast is where miracles happen, girls. Listen carefully to what I am about to say to you. Do not chatter and giggle in the back row there. Maintain silence and clear your thoughts so that this story may remain in your subconscious mind long after I have narrated it. It revolves around the famous Saint Teresa. Her story began in India. She had a special relationship with these mountains. Mother Teresa had tremendous compassion towards humanity, unlike any other person living on this planet. Mother Teresa's heart went out to all the people. Her story begins with her journey in the toy train up to the convent where we are standing today. Her long journey to Darjeeling from the city of Calcutta (now Kolkata) was an auspicious one.

'Mother Teresa was on the cosy seats of the bustling toy train, coming up Hill Cart Road, admiring the natural beauty of this blessed land. With a rosary in her hand, carrying only a small suitcase, she made her way up. On her journey, she looked up at the bright sky when she suddenly received her calling—to serve. Mother Teresa felt a divine presence all around her, asking her to go forth on her mission to help mankind. Serve the poor, help the sick and heal their suffering with her presence. Thus began the story of the Mother Teresa we know today. She arrived at the convent's gates and began her miraculous journey to create the Missionaries of Charity. She began to spread her wisdom within these walls.

'Darjeeling has been a guiding light for Mother Teresa, elevating her from sisterhood to sainthood. This serves as an inspiration to all of us sisters on our path to help mankind and devote our lives to the teachings of Christ. This here, girls, is a story to help you on your own mission on this earth.

'We are all born for a reason, for a higher purpose...and to find that purpose is our ultimate goal. *Temet nosce* (know thyself), my girls. May God bless you and guide you,' she says with a bright smile.

Her words stay in the hearts of the 'convent girls', serving as a beacon of light in the darkest hours. We started referring to this as the 'calling'. A story of hope given to us by our beloved Sister Teresa about the famous Saint Teresa.

28

THE HOUSE OF JEWELS

The Elgin Nor-Khill, our second home, was once the royal guest house of the rulers of Sikkim. The Chogyal, the monarchs of the former Kingdom of Sikkim, have a special place in their hearts for this captivating structure located in the current capital city of Gangtok. Mr Diamond gives me a tour of one of his masterpieces. 'Rea, can you see how sturdy this building is? Its foundation is rock solid,' he says, tapping on the strong white pillars at the entrance. 'This structure was built by the Chogyal himself. It was given a special name, one that holds a deep meaning—something that caught my attention when I walked through its royal gates. The Sikkimese name "Nor-Khill" translates to "the house of jewels". My darling, the jewels are the people, mountains and flora and fauna. These are the true treasures of Sikkim. At the entrance of Nor-Khill is a carefully crafted logo that depicts these jewels, which has been part of the old structure and is still here today, adding to the heritage and historic value of our hotel. The name Nor-Khill stuck with me, as it was chosen by the Chogyal for this guest house, and I decided to continue with the name.'

I walk with Mr Diamond into his house of jewels. 'The King of Sikkim offered Nor-Khill to me himself and invited me to Gangtok to take a look at the property. He wanted it to be in good hands, and I was the perfect candidate as I was already a seasoned hotelier. Today, the original structure of the building has been restored and is well-maintained, which gives The Elgin Nor-Khill a heritage status.'

My father continues, 'My dear, Nor-Khill is deeply connected with Gangtok. It was built by the late king of Sikkim, Tashi Namgyal, in the year 1932. Since its foundation in the 17th century, the Kingdom of Sikkim was threatened by the neighbouring countries of Bhutan, Nepal and China. Sikkim became a part of India much later and still maintains its cultural heritage and ethnicity. It is known to be the cleanest state in India, and is the country's first "organic state". I was drawn to the energy of Sikkim and found myself in Gangtok, the capital of this beautiful state, where The Elgin Nor-Khill is now.'

I walk hand in hand with my father through the double doors of the lobby. He says, 'The royal drawing room is where the king hosted functions for his personal guests and family. We still have a variety of ancient artefacts, traditional furniture, precious photographs of the royal family, paintings by renowned artists, sketches by Mr Douglas and ethnic jewellery, all of which are priceless. Come, have a look at these. We have been hosts to countless dignitaries, political heads, royals, spiritual leaders and film stars from around the world.'

Increasing my pace, I ask, 'Papa, which is your favourite part of the hotel? What made you feel that this property could be your new home?'

He pauses for a second and takes me across the hall. 'This is what anchored me when I stepped into this royal guest house. The incredible view!' My father points towards the sapphire blue sky. Breathing in the fresh air, he says, 'Nor-Khill has a spectacular view of the Palzor football stadium.'

While sipping on a delicious kiwi cocktail, I witness the day's football match. Star players, among them Bhaichung Bhutia and Sunil Chhetri, are like lightning on the field. This extraordinary, ultra-private view is a dream come true for football lovers. Pulling up a chair, I see that the Red Dragon Bar is crowded and that fans are flocking to the Kanchan Gardens on an exciting match day. Sikkim is hosting the match at home, playing against its neighbouring state.

The bedrooms too overlook the Palzor Stadium, and fans are cheering the team from their windows.

'Go, Sikkim! Go!' the home crowd cheers.

The ambience is absolutely spectacular.

On a clear sunny day, when the clouds are not blanketing the Kanchenjunga, I peep at the mountain range. It is almost like the mountains have come out to say hello to the spectators. Once the crowd has scattered and the game is over, our house becomes peaceful again.

∽

The month of November brings with it a pink blanket of cherry blossoms that enhances the beauty of the mountains. My father planted the cherry blossom tree at Nor-Khill, which reflects his innermost love for nature. I sit beneath the blossoming tree while listening to instrumental music and feel the pink petals falling over my head, transporting me into a realm of enchantment. Neighbouring poinsettias bloom blood red and stand out in contrast to the cherry blossoms dancing in the breeze. I close my eyes and slowly drift into deep meditation. Breathing in and out...keeping my focus on my breath, I let endless thoughts ride away from my mind. Calmness fills my soul and my mind becomes a blank slate. I can sense the universe inside me—the whole universe. I flow towards a space of stillness. Silence. I feel nothing to feel everything... the house of jewels brings out this side of me.

The reason that makes The Elgin Nor-Khill special is the Sikkimese cuisine. The three-course candlelight meal draws me back to the hotel every time. Dim flames light up my mood. The romantic and soothing ambience in the Shangri-La dining room is an unforgettable and sumptuous experience. The strong smell of butter and garlic fills the air as silver trays arrive from the kitchen. My family specifically relishes the variety of Sikkimese delicacies served in the authentic and traditional style by our competent chef, who was once the personal cook to the late Chogyal of Sikkim. Wining and dining in the grand hall makes one feel like a royal. Our house of jewels exudes charm and is on par with any royal palace around the world.

First arrives a bowl of steaming hot chimney soup for starters, called gyako; up next is the traditional (fermented) millet beer called tongba, served with boiling water, which is something to die for. Tongba is Jethi's favourite too, which makes The Elgin Nor-Khill her favourite among all our homes. Local to Sikkim, this drink is served in a tall handmade wooden jar (also called the tongba). The fermented millet, when mature, is put into the tongba and is then filled up to the brim with boiling water. This drink may appear harmless, but it can intoxicate you, putting you into a deep sleep. Jethi's love for Sikkimese tongba, our otherwise pious nanny, reflects an unusual side to her personality that is different from that of a strict disciplinarian.

Apart from the splendid cuisine, the gorgeous gardens are also a main attraction. Known as the Kanchan Garden, deriving its name from the holy Kanchenjunga mountain range, it was named by the Chogyal himself. It was his favourite spot. The state flower of Sikkim is the noble dendrobium, which blooms throughout the hotel gardens.

Apart from us, the hotel also has another host who brings a smile to everyone's face even on the gloomiest of days. Our Russian Samoyeds—Hilton and Paris—always come to greet us, full of love and enthusiasm. These two snowballs are the friendliest among us all; they even have a fan following of their own. They are The Elgin's celebrities. Whenever I look out of my windows, I see them either basking in the sun or rolling around in the garden below. Visitors love their company and have titled them stars of The Elgin Nor-Khill.

My father has a subtle sense of humour. He named the dogs as an inside joke. This adorable pair had a litter of puppies, all of whom were sent to our different homes in Kalimpong, Darjeeling and Pelling, where they are spreading warmth and happiness. Without these adorable furballs, The Elgin experience is incomplete. They are a part of our family.

29

HOSTING THE SPIRITUAL LEADER

The Elgin Nor-Khill once had the honour of hosting one of the most revered personalities in the spiritual world. His presence within our walls was the greatest blessing that could have been bestowed upon The Elgin family. A large group of monks visited Gangtok for the famous Kalachakra ceremony and stayed in The Elgin Nor-Khill for 41 days. Kalachakra means the wheel of time. This tradition originated during the early decades of the eleventh century in ancient India.

Many Buddhist devotees from different parts of the world participate in this festival. This tradition is significant for Buddhists as it is based on Gautama Buddha's teachings of non-duality and achieving a state of enlightened awareness. Till today, this tradition is carried on in the Buddhist world by monks.

A day or two before the spiritual leader arrived at Nor-Khill, a large group of monks came to the hotel to inspect the premises and prepare it for his arrival. The monks, clad in red kasaya, arrived to ensure that appropriate arrangements were in place for the spiritual leader. The Elgin Nor-Khill was inspected, and police officers were stationed at the entrance. After all, we were expecting the arrival of one of the most famous and important personalities of all time. My family was extremely excited to host such an extraordinary guest.

Jethi was jumping up and down in her blue bakhu

when she heard about his visit. She said, 'Do not disturb or infuriate me at any time. I want to cleanse my body of anger, hatred, greed and envy.' She prayed for days on end before the spiritual leader's arrival so that she could stand in his holy presence. She began a cleansing process, and it involved all of us too. Jethi has subconsciously trained our entire family in the Buddhist ways of life for years. She is a big influence in our lives, which is especially evident in us siblings. She often took us to monasteries with her and explained the Buddha's teachings to us. Her philosophical mind and peaceful chants were embedded in us as we grew up. With Jethi in the house, the preparations for the grand arrival had begun.

The congregation of monks arrived, laden with everything one could imagine. They brought with them a bed, chairs and Tibetan carpets meant only for him, prayer flags, side tables, blankets and even curtains. They brought with them whatever the spiritual leader would need during his visit.

The monks cleared out the entire building. They had rearranged the interiors like it was a puzzle. Not even a single piece of furnishing was left; nothing that belonged to the hotel was left inside the premises. 'It is believed that the spiritual leader should only be surrounded by his furniture and a select group of monks during his visit,' our concierge, who is also Tibetan, said. He knew the customs. The managing staff of the hotel were dismissed, including the chefs in the kitchen, and even the gardeners in the lawn. The kitchen was re-arranged and converted into something completely different from what it looked like on a usual day. The monks performed a series of cleansing ceremonies at the hotel. They chanted prayers and did not leave even a single room unturned. The sound of conch shells and fragrance of lemongrass incense engulfed the hotel. They conducted the cleansing ritual with sandalwood sticks and camphor.

There was a palpable shift in the environment; I could smell and see it everywhere. It had to be perfect for the arrival of this holy man. More than perfect, it had to be divine. Police patrols did regular rounds around The Elgin Nor-Khill.

The monks brought their own entourage of cooks and people to look after his every need. Every single thing the leader touched had to be pure and was brought by the monks with them. The intense purification and rearrangement of the premises took 2–3 days, and the monks performed their chores rigorously, without even a moment's break. No one was allowed to be within the hotel premises. By 'no one' they meant not even us. The owners were not allowed inside either! My father spoke to the head monk, and he finally agreed to let us stay in the hotel but only on one condition. We had to live in the adjacent wing, a stone's throw from the main building. The old wing was going to be our home for a few days. At least we still had a good view.

This experience will always stay with us because we were hosting one of the most revered man on the planet, and also because we were not allowed to stay within the main building of our own premises. We would also remember because never before had we witnessed the conversion of the interiors of any of our hotels into an elaborate Buddhist monastery. The Elgin Nor-Khill became a fortress overnight. The monks made mandalas at the entrance and adorned the garden with prayer flags. The stage was set for his arrival.

Jethi competed with the monks when it came to cleansing and purifying all of us. She prayed non-stop, ignoring us if we dared to interrupt her meditation.

Finally, the day arrived. The spiritual leader stepped into

our hotel. Large crowds had gathered in the outer perimeters of the hotel, and people—dressed in traditional outfits—were chanting his name. I had never witnessed such a spectacular sight in my life. It felt like I was in an imaginary world. A huge crowd gathered in the Palzor Stadium for the Kalachakra ceremony. It was a magnificent sight. I witnessed the spiritual leader walking through the crowd of devotees, giving his blessings to each individual on his path.

Thousands of people swarmed the spiritual leader, yet he noticed an old lady praying quietly in the distance. The spiritual master walked all the way, moving through the horde of people, to where she was standing. He blessed the old lady and left her teary-eyed. I too had an overwhelming feeling of being touched by an enlightened being. His greatness lies in his compassion and humbleness towards mankind.

As the day went on, we had the opportunity to meet him and take his blessings. Jethi, however, was absolutely star-struck. She had been preparing for this moment for months. Finally, the day had arrived to meet him in the flesh. My family humbly took his blessings with our hands folded in a namaste. Aanyaa, standing in his presence, felt a flash of gold all around this holy man. She took me aside and said, 'Rea, I can see a bright golden aura around him. His crown chakra is emitting golden hues with white light scattered around his physical body. I have never seen such a powerful aura around any human being before. His aura is all-encompassing and I feel a divine pull towards it. His energy is magnanimous.' We were lost in his auric field while my father had a long conversation with him. He laid his hands on our heads and blessed us. He then reached out to bless our prayer beads. He was carrying an apple with him and, to my surprise, he handed it over to me. As we are not Tibetans, he asked Jethi if she was the one responsible for teaching us the ways of Buddhism. Jethi quietly nodded her head, not uttering a word out of respect for him. He gave her the largest smile of acknowledgement and blessed her. Jethi was so overwhelmed by this gesture that till today, she cannot help but repeat this tale to all her friends in the community. She became the centre of attention that day as she stood in his presence and had the opportunity to be blessed by him.

With a large golden aura extending to the open skies above, the spiritual leader spread his light on our land.

30

THE FOUR MAGICAL CAVES OF SIKKIM

'Sikkim is a land that embodies the spiritual way of life in today's modern world. It is a sacred space dotted with mystical caves and landforms that are religiously significant. There are ancient caves situated in four different directions in Sikkim's mountains, which also appear in Buddhist texts. Since the beginning of evolution, Hindu and Buddhist traditions have considered caves as places of refuge, hermitage and wisdom. Monks and yogis practice deep meditation in Himalayan caves that are believed to hold the divine knowledge of the enlightened beings who meditated before them in these quiet spaces. Only a few monks are aware of the presence of these particular caves, who preserve the knowledge within and pass it on to a select group of lamas,' my mother says.

One evening, as I am taking a stroll in the Kanchan Garden of The Elgin Nor-Khill in Gangtok, I come across a Buddhist monk clad in maroon kasaya, sitting with his legs crossed on the wet grass, near a blossoming camellia bush, admiring its beauty. I can't help but think how peaceful this monk looked, lost in the world of nature.

I join the monk, exchange a cordial smile and a friendly greeting and ask politely, 'Tashi Delek, are you a guest at the hotel? Or have you come for tea?'

'I am on a pilgrimage. I have come from Bodh Gaya and will travel all the way to the upper Himalayas. To the hidden land,' the monk says in a soft tone.

Over my conversation with him, I could sense in my heart that I was on to something mystical and enchanting. The monk reveals details about his pilgrimage as he says, 'I am here on a special mission. A divine calling. I am here to visit the four sacred caves of Sikkim.'

Suddenly, I have goosebumps all over my arms. I cover myself with a denim jacket and listen to the wise monk speak. Meanwhile, I request for The Elgin's Honey Trap, a hot ginger honey drink. The monk, with wooden prayer beads in his hand, gazes into the distance and continues, 'The four caves are spread in four different directions of Sikkim, forming a cross with the small town of Tashiding at the very centre. The caves in the north, south, east and west make Tashiding one of the holiest places on land. It is known as the heart of the spiritual world—an impression of Mount Meru on Earth. It is believed that Guru Padmasambhava sanctified these caves. My pilgrimage will begin at Tashiding, and then I will be going clockwise to all four caves.

'Towards the north lies the holiest cave of them all, known as the "Heart of the Gods Cave". In the south lies the "Secret Cave of the Dakinis" and in the east is the "Secret Cave" while towards the west lies the "Cave of Great Happiness", which purportedly prolongs one's life span. Each of these four caves is situated in a remote area, making it inaccessible by road. It takes determination and enthusiasm to reach the desired destination. Because it is unknown to many, no motorable roads have been constructed to reach these sacred caves. The only way in or out of these locations is by foot.

'The cave up north is the most difficult to get to; the journey is an entire day's walk from the town of Lapdang. It is a two-day journey through the untamed Khangchendzonga

National Park. The Himalayan people believe our Gods live in these sacred Himalayas. The cave towards the west, known as the "Cave of Great Happiness", is in a very discreet location as well. It is an entire day's walk from the town of Pelling,' the monk whispers, gazing up at the Himalayas.

I feel overwhelmed upon hearing about this particular cave because it's situated somewhere near Pemayangtse. I have explored the entire terrain of West Sikkim by now and yet, I somehow missed the "Cave of Great Happiness". The Elgin Mount Pandim is my home and still, this cave is unknown to me. A trip to the "Cave of Great Happiness" is immediately added to my Pemayangtse to-do list.

The lama continues, 'The cave in the east, known as the "Secret Cave", is at a distance of about five kilometres from the town of Ravangla. To reach this cave, one has to walk downhill for an hour through slippery slopes until one locates the hills of Maenam and Tendong. The "Secret Cave" lies somewhere in between these two hills; as its name implies, its location is unknown to many.'

'The cave towards the south is the "Khando-sangphu", which literally means the "Secret Cave of the Dakinis". It is located among the Himalayan hot springs of Reshi. A narrow suspension bridge over the river Rangeet is the first landmark on your journey. As you enter the cave, you can see small handprints on the walls, said to be left by the dakinis. An image of Goddess Tara is decorated with wildflowers and the cave is lit with butter lamps.'

The Reshi Hot Springs is a place where we rejuvenate and relax while in Pemayangtse. These sacred hot springs are high in natural minerals and have miraculous healing abilities. I have floated in their rich medicinal healing waters with Aanyaa, enjoying our natural spa sessions. The presence of sulphur in the water keeps it constantly warm in the winter months, making it apt for a relaxing dip.

The wise lama starts chanting *Om Mani Padme Hum*. His eyes remain closed as he says, 'There lies a quaint Buddhist shrine at each of these caves, with an appointed lama who conducts prayers and gives offerings to the resident deities. The sacred ritual is conducted by specific monks who pass down the knowledge of these secret caves only to the members of their community. As one enters these caves, one can see prayer flags adorning the interiors and breathe in the lingering sweetness of incense. These caves date back hundreds of years and are still well preserved naturally, almost like they are frozen in time. If anyone feels a magnetic pull from these caves, it would be a calling from the resident deities protecting them. Our sacred space is meant to be undisturbed and kept in its former pure glory. It invites those whose hearts are clear as quartz, whose intentions are as light as air. You should not tread here with the motive of selfish gain or to disturb the natural ecosystem surrounding it. It is to be discovered only with the intention of reaching one's meditative state of enlightenment.'

Caves give me a sense of reaching back to the source of life—a mother's womb. It is all-encompassing and liberating. It helps one focus on the true self and to break away from this world. I say to the monk, 'Here...take this camellia flower with you and place it on your sacred shrine. It seems like the cosmos intended for us to meet.'

The wise lama stands up and calmly walks away towards the gates of The Elgin Nor-Khill.

31

THE HIDDEN LAND OF DRAGONS

Jethi guides me into the mystical realm of Sikkim. 'The land of wonders—Sikkim has many names given to it because of its mesmerizing nature. It is known as the hidden land among the various tribes of Sikkim. The land and its people are my unshakeable roots,' says my Tibetan nanny. Sikkim is the land of abundant natural waterfalls, lakes and verdant valleys. Its roaring rivers flow from the snow-capped mountains of the Kanchenjunga. The sweet aroma of cardamom floats through the paddy fields and lifts my senses.

'My dear, hold this soil in your hand. Feel its richness. This is the real treasure. We evolve from this soil to go back to it when we die—the circle of life.' And just like that, Jethi takes me into her world, rolling her white prayer beads as we gaze into the distant mountains of the hidden land. After the harsh landscape of the Tibetan Plateau comes to an end, we enter the lush terrain of Sikkim. This mountain haven holds a very significant place in the pages of history and ancient religious texts, tucked away in the Himalayas. It borders Bhutan, Nepal and Tibet. With her eyes locked on the Himalayan range, Jethi says, 'Rea, it is believed that many enlightened beings have walked upon these sacred lands and blessed the deep blue mountains. His Holiness, the 14th Dalai Lama, the spiritual leader of Tibetan Buddhism, has a deep-rooted love for this land as Sikkim was the gateway for his escape after the annexation of Tibet, his birthplace. The pilgrimage from the deserted north into this lush valley is described as "a heavenly abode" for travellers, down the treacherous silk route that even my grandfather journeyed.'

Rolling landscapes filled with dense vegetation and wildflowers welcome you to the land of the Gods. Landlocked and tucked among the Himalayas, it is known as the last Shangri-La on Earth. A place of pure consciousness and divinity. Himalayan monks and yogis have come looking for Shambhala, only to fall short of discovering it. Jethi continues, 'I connect to Shambhala while in deep meditation. My child, Shambhala is a realm that exists in the astral plane. Just close your eyes to disconnect from your physical reality to connect to the higher realm.' Jethi's words guide my way into the heart of this land.

Guru Padmasambhava, known as one of the founding fathers of Tibetan Buddhism, regarded Sikkim as the most sacred centre of pilgrimage, bodhisattvas, enlightenment, peace and happiness. If you are in search of a realm outside the mundane life, this is the land of miracles and astral forces that you should seek. The vibration of Sikkim is unlike any other landmass in existence. The Himalayan flora is unlike any you have seen before, the exotic birds sing in harmony and the mind is empty of its billion galloping thoughts. A place where you can be still, stay calm and feel the energy field around you. The natural lakes, hot springs known for their medicinal and therapeutic values, glaciers, gushing waterfalls, sacred caves, valley of flowers and forests tell the story of an untouched land. The Sikkimese mostly follow the teachings of the Buddha and their hearts are as pure as the land they live on.

Holding my cold hand, my wise nanny says, 'Every life is precious to us in the Himalayas. It may be that of an ant or a snow leopard. A soul takes a different form in each birth. It depends on our karma in each life. This is why I refrain from harming any living thing. I release even a large and poisonous spider into the wild instead of killing it. You never know whose soul resides within whom in this circle of life.' Ancient monasteries, holy stupas and stone structures blend with the landscape, creating a haven for spiritual transcendence. To call this hidden land also my home is definitely a blessing for me.

∽

The bright rays of the afternoon sun shine upon us as I impatiently wait for the day to begin. I sit on the moist grass, my fingers stroking the water droplets clinging to its blades, which feels like nature shedding tears of joy after the monsoon rains cleansed her aura into lighter hues.

It's 3.01 p.m. and I see my father with an officer in the Red Dragon Bar, relishing a cup of white tea. He looks at me through the window and says, 'Rea, enjoying yourself I see. Seems like the dragons are about to appear in the clear sky. Let's wait and see what tonight brings into our house of jewels. Get ready for the night!' On hearing his words, I quietly wait for the clock to shift its hand.

When we enter the state of Sikkim, a long bridge—its sides dotted with Buddhist prayer flags—connects it with West Bengal. On the border, there are elaborate dragon statues with intricate designs of lotus and the seven jewels of Sikkim. The vibrant colours of the gate to Sikkim fight for my attention along with the emblem of the state—two dragons facing each other and supporting a blazon that consists of a lotus within a chain of 12 annulets, which symbolizes purity. The dragons seem to welcome us observers to the state, which was once known as the hidden land of dragons. Enormous colourful dragon emblems, with fire blazing from the dragon's mouths, are scattered all over the terrain. Further, dragons are also present in the form of statues engraved on large gates of buildings, monasteries and the king's palace, acting as their guardians. Dragons are also crafted on handmade tables called 'choktses' as well as thankas; their designs are woven into the local attires and carpets and carved on ethnic silver jewellery by local craftspeople.

The clock strikes seven and I see a cumulonimbus of clouds in the dark sky. I hear their rumbling, which sounds almost like the beating drums of an impending war. Tonight is special; a grand celebration is about to begin at The Elgin Nor-Khill as we celebrate renewal and rebirth within our walls, but the host is still glued to her dressing table.

I am wearing an indigo duchess satin gown with a golden tassel sash around my waist. I style my hair into a classic chignon with side tendrils. After applying black eyeliner, I add some gold glitter around my eyes. I apply rose pink lipstick and add the final touch—my grandmother's Burmese ruby earrings, bracelet and necklace. They seem to imitate the flaming fire of the oncoming dragons. With lavender sprayed on my wrist, I make my way down to the Shangri-La Hall to engage in a conversation with my chardonnay. The drums are beating, which heralds the Tibetan dance of dragons and snow lions. They shake up The Elgin Nor-Khill with their thundering steps. Nor-Khill or 'The House of Jewels' has turned into the 'House of Dragons'. The sweet incense of lemongrass floats in the fresh air as the vibrance of these traditional dancers engulfs me. The Kanchan Garden is lit with outdoor lanterns, and the Sikkimese dragon dance seems to be spreading the power of their flames. One can see symbols of these mythical winged creatures on many artefacts throughout the hotel and on the furniture, the walls in the Shangri-La dining room, the Red Dragon Bar, encompassing the architecture of The Elgin Nor-Khill, situated in the capital city of Gangtok, thus making it the dragon's den. Dragons are our 'astral mascots'.

I notice my father in the distance and walk up to him. My mind is seeking answers to questions regarding the significance of these dragons dancing in our Himalayan home. Mr Diamond is a living encyclopaedia of myths and legends. With a snifter of brandy in his hand, he whispers in his sweet voice, 'My dear, I am glad your mind is full of curiosity. Only when you ask the right questions, do you get the right answers. Do not follow anything blindly without knowing its true meaning, Rea. Dragons are a symbol of prosperity and wisdom in ancient Sikkimese culture. They are revered as the spirit guides of this land throughout history. Himalayan culture is driven by symbolic representations that decode our universe. The dragon represents all the four elements that exist on earth—fire, earth, water and air. It is a symbol of totality, unity, strength of the mind, power and wisdom. It is an all-powerful symbol. It represents the spiritual, cultural and religious aspects of the people of the Himalayan belt. Dragons hold significant meaning in their fierce yet magical nature. One of the myths of the creation of our world revolves around these magnificent creatures. Legend has it that in the vast expanse of space, a dragon and a phoenix collided, creating infinite ripples— an unstoppable energy with extraordinary pace. This cosmic encounter resulted in a series of power struggles between these two fiery beings, which led to a peaceful dance when both accepted each other's power—a clash that ultimately bound them. Then, life erupted in the dark space. This is why dragons are a symbol of creation. A manifestation of yin and yang, just like the dance of life by the dragon and the phoenix.' My father, being a brilliant orator, held my undivided attention with his charismatic words. An expert in history and mythology, Papa has an answer to everything. This is why his company, with his insights and knowledge, is food for the soul.

I slowly move back to the Kanchan Garden and begin to take it all in. I wander to a time when history and mythology merged to create such a fascinating concept. A desire, a strange craving echoes through my curious mind, looking for more ancient knowledge. My spirit hungers for more unknown tales that are afloat in this hidden land. I notice my mother walking towards me dressed in a flowing black gown. A dragon bracelet clasped around her wrist, intricately rendered with an ombré shine, instantly catches my eye.

'What a beautiful bracelet you have, Mama. I haven't seen this piece in your jewellery box before. It's crafted entirely of metal, I see. Quite unlike your taste. You usually prefer slender pieces of gemstone jewellery, don't you?'

My mother unclasps the bracelet and slides it onto my wrist. The bracelet opens from the centre and clasps firmly on my wrist. My mother says, 'This bracelet is a special one. It is known as "panchaloha" in ancient Vedic sciences. It's a combination of five sacred metals melted together to boost health, good fortune and abundance. The five alloys of gold, silver, copper, lead and iron intertwine into the dragon's body. It gives strength and resistance to the person wearing it. I had one crafted by our family jeweller with two gold dragon heads to highlight this significance. A circle of life we all live in.' The metal of the bracelet touching my skin may be cold but it feels like a bonfire warming up my body. I look around for my sister and find her enjoying the night in the company of a flaming dragon tequila and, to my surprise, a handsome young stranger. Dressed in a baby pink gown, I see her pale cheeks turn pink like petunias, blushing in this young man's company. I hate to interrupt her conversation, but I have an itch to be the thorn in this love bush.

'Aanyaa! Aanyaa! Over here!' I wave to her, shining the light of my cell phone towards the sky. I quickly walk past the dancing dragons and steal her away from the celebration and the young man.

'Rea, what is it? Why are we going to the indoor lounge? I want to stay in the Kanchan Garden. I met someone interesting. This better be important, Rea,' my sister says, relishing a dragon rum ball.

'Yes, I can see by your flushed cheeks how urgent it is, Aanyaa. It looks like someone has picked a partner for the next dance. Oh, how romantic! This is why I have stolen you away from the guy. I need you to do a pendulum reading for me. Please don't be mad. I need a small and simple answer.'

My pretty sister goes to the powder room, comes out and is then ready to be my oracle.

'Gosh! The things you make me do, little sister,' Aanyaa murmurs in her fortune-telling avatar.

I watch as she takes off her dragon-shaped Himalayan quartz pendant and places it under running water for a few seconds. She cleanses the crystal's energy and asks me to be ready for the pendulum reading.

'Rea, while I cleanse the air with sage, do me a favour and grab a matchbox from the table. I need you to light this Himalayan rock salt candle and connect to its growing flame.'

The aroma fills our fresh Himalayan air with a salty essence. The red flame of a baby pink candle transports me into Cupid's den, igniting a passion that is waiting to be unleashed. I take a piece of paper and divide it into two halves with a stroke of black ink. I write the words 'yes' and 'no' on a clean sheet and wait for Aanyaa to begin her session.

I watch Aanyaa as she gently dangles her clear quartz over the piece of paper. The locket swings from left to right. It moves freely over the paper directly for a few seconds.

'Rea, now think of your question with a clear head and let the pendulum stop on the answer to your question.'

I focus my energy on my request and ask the cosmic fire to guide me to my flame. 'Angels, guide me! Is newness coming into my life? Is a special person about to step into my life?'

I watch as Aanyaa's pendulum swings from side to side, making a final stop at an answer.

'Praise the angels, the answer is a positive one. It stopped on "yes"!' Aanyaa says with a pleasant smile.

I feel joyous and satisfied with my energy reading. 'Yes, Aanyaa, thank you, my sweet cupcake! It's just the answer I was hoping for. Now I can enjoy watching the snow lions dancing in the Kanchan Garden while I await Cupid's arrow to strike me. My soulmate is about to arrive. I can feel it in my bones. This is why I have been getting so curious lately. I feel as though I am about to be swept away by love's tide coming my way! I sense my knight somewhere in the sky.'

This is for you, my unknown heart. For I am in love before laying my eyes on you. When I see you, the mountains will be covered by waves. When you see me, the oceans will erupt into flames. This one's for you, my other half.

32

THE SECRETS OF THE RUMTEK MONASTERY

A short drive away from Gangtok, the capital of Sikkim, lies the mystical Rumtek Monastery, which is the seat of various relics of the ancient Buddhist world. I have come here before, especially for a meditation session with the resident monks. It was an uplifting and positive experience that really helped me gather myself and put my scattered energy into focus.

This monastery is one of the most peaceful places near Gangtok. Also called the Dharma Chakra Centre, its ancient walls are charged with vibrations way beyond our frequency. At first glance, it appears to be an ordinary Buddhist monastery, with prayer wheels decorated along the walkway but, as you venture deeper into the grounds, it opens up hidden secrets. A land where legends entwine with religious beliefs. These legends are passed down through sacred texts and divine art forms that are found within the monastery. The smell of oil-laden lamps and young monks playing football in the courtyard brings a smile to my face. I visited this place many times as a child but now, visiting this place again as an adult seems to be affecting me differently. I want to investigate the history of the monastery and look into the various folklore surrounding its existence.

This time, I take a guide with me who explains the significance of the place along with its gripping legends. As I walk in, I clear my mind of its various thoughts, turning it into an empty vessel, a chalice, ready to expand the hidden dimensions of my mind. My guide explains that Rumtek is part of one of the many schools of Buddhism, called Karma Kagyu. He also explains the significance of this place and why His Holiness the Dalai Lama frequently visits this monastery. 'Rumtek is said to be the seat of the "Karmapas". This monastery was founded in the sixteenth century but was refurbished by the sixteenth Karmapa who came to Sikkim from Tibet. He was in exile and took Rumtek to be his home of solace. He found a sense of tranquillity in this monastery and began to impart his teachings to various monks who looked to him for guidance. His body is preserved within a golden stupa with many priceless relics in the monastery. It is considered to be a shrine. Lighting incense is a form of worship, which purifies the sacred space.'

The strong smell of camphor burning in the courtyard leads me into the sacred monastery. As the conversation continues, I am intrigued by what my guide has to say. During my previous visits to Rumtek, I did not ask many questions, but this time, I want to know what this monastery has been hiding within itself. My curious mind is seeking some answers. I hear a strange calling from this energized place—*seek and you shall find*. This came to my mind in that very instant. Like a ringing in my head. A higher force at play.

I check my wristwatch as I stand between the pillars of wisdom. It is 11.11 a.m. A moment of synchronized events. My intimate interaction with the cosmos through binary numbers. The language of the universe. I follow my thirst for knowledge and head out to seek answers.

My guide starts the tour by explaining the origin of the monastery. He clears his throat and says, 'The Karmapas are known as the Black Hat Lamas.' I notice ancient paintings on the walls, called 'thankas', depicting the Karmapas with black crowns on their heads. It's something I have never seen other Buddhist lamas or monks wear. 'This black hat symbolizes the divine power of the Karmapas. Only the chosen ones were allowed to wear this distinct black hat. Legend has it that the first Karmapa was visited by several astral fairies known as "Dakinis" in Tibetan Buddhism. Dakinis are called "sky dancers" who bestowed on the Karmapa a precious gift during their arrival in the human realm. Each fairy offered a strand of their beautiful black hair that held divine magical powers. They asked the first Karmapa to cherish this and keep it as a form of blessing for the kingdom. It is strictly to be held by the Karmapa himself and is handed down through generations to the next Karmapa. This is a form of astral coronation. The other-worldly hair strands of these dakinis were woven into the black hat we see the Karmapa wearing today. This relic is safeguarded in the Rumtek Monastery and it is believed that if the hat is not adorned by the Karmapa, it should be kept away safely in an airtight box. Legends hold warnings that if the instructions are not followed accurately then the black hat will fly away, disappearing back into the realm of the fairies,' my guide says, catching my attention. I begin to feel butterflies in my stomach. It rings a bell in my mind, one that is already curious about exploring other dimensions of existence.

The sweet aroma of sandalwood guides me to a colourful wall. I gaze into an ancient painting of a dakini wearing a crown of flowers underneath an arch of red flames. Her golden body is slender, like a sparkling chalice. I walk past a jewelled pagoda with a golden stupa that is studded with turquoise stones.

I ask my guide if I can take a look at the black hat but he shakes his head, saying the hat is kept away in secrecy till the new Karmapa takes his seat in the Rumtek Monastery. Only a select few lamas know its location.

33

HIDDEN GOLD

The mysterious Himalayas, covered in snow, consist of unknown realms, still not marked by the footprints of man. It is truly terra incognita, containing a universe within a universe. My sister and I dig deep to uncover precious Himalayan gold. This treasure is only found in the high mountainous regions of Tibet, Nepal and India, making it a treasured part of our ecosystem. Secrecy and exclusivity surround an incredible medicinal mushroom called *yarsagumba*, making the fungus more expensive than gold itself. It is a priceless gift from Mother Nature, cherished and protected by the untamed landscape of the Himalayas.

Yarsagumba (yartsa gunbu) means 'grass' in the summer and 'worm' in the winter in Tibetan. Not many people know of the existence of this mysterious 'plant'; they are about two to three inches in size. This 'plant' is an unusual blend of nature. The *yarsagumba* comprises a rare fungus growing out of the head of a dead caterpillar. Their location is very hard to come by in the treacherous hills. Only shepherds living in the forests know of its existence. If you ask the locals for information regarding the *yarsagumba*, they may avoid the topic altogether. This cold response is because of the high degree of exploitation of the land, which attracts many people from around the world who pose a threat to the local inhabitants and the natural vegetation of the terrain.

On my journey to the Indo–Tibetan border towards the holy Gurudongmar Lake along with my sister, my young chauffeur shed light, for the first time, on this mysterious Himalayan gold. My chauffeur says, 'Madam, can I tell you a secret? This medicinal 'herb' is also known as Himalayan Viagra. The local shepherds, along with the grazing animals, such as yaks, come to consume these naturally, which boosts their libido. If you carefully observe the terrain, the population of Himalayan yaks has increased rapidly due to its consumption. Now, let me reveal the real magic of the *yarsagumba*. The most astonishing fact, the one that hooked my attention is that this 'herb' is secretly meant to boost the lifespan of its consumers.' The young man's words draw me in as he reveals the astonishing nature of this fungus.

Rolling an oval emerald ring on my finger I begin a round of questions and answers with this knowledgeable man. 'You know this terrain pretty well I see,' I say, while watching him navigate the zigzagging roads.

'Yes, Madam, each bend in these Himalayan roads is etched in my memory. Well, can I tell you something? This secret gold of the forest is closely guarded by the inhabitants of the nearby villages. It is very difficult to come by as the local shepherds have to go into dangerous uncharted territories, sometimes even risking their lives, just to collect a few of these. The Himalayas can be very dangerous due to its uneven structure and slippery rock formations. The mountains can be very unforgiving at times. One has to have advanced mountaineering skills to get to the fungus' breeding site. This is one of the reasons why the *yarsagumba* is not easily accessible, even by the local tribes. It specifically grows at an altitude of 10,000–16,000 feet. Its miraculous quality of increasing the lifespan and boosting libido makes it even more valuable. Local

Himalayan tribes consume this by making a thin paste and adding it to warm milk or water. I have taken it too, Madam. Milk is usually preferable. I have to warn you though that its unique taste may not suit everyone's palate. The closest I can come to describing the taste of the *yarsagumba* is that it tastes like raw mushroom. It is a little sour, though mostly neutral on the tongue. The local inhabitants claim that it gives them an immense amount of energy, helps them function in these harsh mountains and increases the body's tolerance to extremely cold weather. Mountain folk usually have a long lifespan, and their life expectancy goes up to 90 years! Madam, what do you think? Do I look fit and youthful to you? Can you guess my age?' the chauffeur says while running his hands through his short dark hair.

Aanyaa and I giggle at this man's humour and make a wild guess. 'Hmm... Are you in your early thirties?' The chauffeur, full of pride, replies, 'No, Madam, I am forty-six years old!' We are stunned by the chauffeur's declaration. 'Well, it looks like the *yarsagumba* certainly works its magic. You have convinced me to try it,' I say.

As we drive down the bumpy roads, we observe elderly people on the porches of their homes, busy with their daily prayers. 'Madam, look around you. For them, this 'herb' is a blessing from their mountain deities to help the community thrive,' our chauffeur explains. 'Many foreign nationals come to Sikkim in search of this 'plant' but fail to gather it as it is such a rare find. It is used in various Tibetan and Chinese medicines. These species grow naturally on Tibet's land. Tibet is said to hold many natural wonders in its vast landscape—this rare fungus is just one of its wonders. The Himalayan ecosystem is unlike any other, making it a land of hidden treasures.'

34

THE LEGEND OF GURUDONGMAR LAKE

The Gurudongmar Lake is mesmerizing and mystical and named after Guru Padmasambhava. It has a spiritual significance, as it makes one feel close to the mythical land of Shambhala. It stands calm under snow-capped mountains that feed the waters of this glittering lake. Its water is so clear and untouched by human activity that it reflects the azure sky—as above, so below.

One of the highest lakes in the world, its location is a challenge for visitors because of the harsh terrain and low oxygen levels. As Aanyaa and I go up this rugged expanse, our auric field begins to be engulfed by this powerful force of nature.

Narrow roads and bends in the Himalayan mountains can get a little scary along the path. Several military cantonments are present in this area and one can visit this lake only with the permission of the Indian army. The Gurudongmar Valley that leads to the lake is a long stretch of gravel and black sand, surrounded by snow-capped ranges.

While the car passes through this terrain, the landscape changes dramatically with every turn and I feel a churning in my stomach. We arrive at a flat plateau after a steep climb, which takes hours to traverse. The journey is a visual delight for every nature lover. This offbeat terrain is the holy grail for adventure seekers...but it's certainly not for the faint-hearted.

We drive onwards from the town of Lachen, passing numerous waterfalls and gazing at wild horses on both sides of the road; small bridges with fluttering Tibetan prayer flags energize this holy land. In the old days, the journey was not an easy one; pilgrims would either walk or ride on horseback to reach the lake. The journey would take them weeks, and sometimes even months. It is a treacherous climb and prayer flags provided the necessary boost, as many pilgrims would lose their lives, unable to complete their quest to reach the sacred plateau.

Even today, with motorable roads and various modes of transport, the journey is not an easy one. I can imagine the amount of courage the mountain dwellers need to make this holy journey. No wonder the popular saying still stands true today. *What matters is the journey and not the destination.*

Our young Sikkimese chauffeur moves swiftly through this uneven terrain. With the car engine rumbling, we begin discussing the land and the history associated with it as well as various facts, myths and legends surrounding Gurudongmar that only the locals living here have information about. Our conversation lasts for around five to six hours as we cross the dangerous bends.

The young man says, 'Legend has it that Guru Padmasambhava, on his journey from Tibet to India, came across the Gurudongmar Lake. Local villagers were facing a shortage of water as the lake was mostly frozen throughout the year. They did not have access to clean water, which decreased their chance of survival in this hostile plateau and was a major concern. Their suffering was brought to the guru's attention. Guru Padmasambhava, a compassionate man, felt for the locals and made his way towards the massive frozen lake. He laid his hands on the thick ice sheet covering the water underneath and channelled his energy into it. Since then, miraculously, that particular area where he laid his hands remains unfrozen—even during the harshest of winters. The villagers were overjoyed with this blessing and built a quaint monastery at a distance in honour of Guru Padmasambhava. The lake was thus given the name "Gurudongmar" in honour of Guru Padmasambhava.' Clearing his throat, he continues, 'This lake is also one of the source streams of the Teesta River and is considered holy by Hindus, Buddhists and Sikhs alike. The Sikhs believe that their patron saint, Guru Nanak, walked past this lake. Many Sikhs visit this lake during the summer months when on a pilgrimage to Gurudwara Nanaklama in Chungthang.'

Aanyaa, paying complete attention to his words, shifts her gaze towards me and says, 'Rea, Gurudongmar Lake is an embodiment of irresistible beauty and positive vibrations. I am looking forward to laying my eyes on her. I feel a strange calling from this lake as if it is waiting for me.'

The chauffeur then goes on to tell us about another mysterious fact about this lake. In a serious tone, he says, 'Madams, the higher altitude makes it difficult to breathe, because of which we are allowed to stay only for a fixed duration of about twenty minutes. Many people who visit have to adapt to the higher altitude and usually stay for an hour at the military base, which is a two-hour drive from the lake. Visitors carry oxygen masks along with them to deal with less oxygen in the atmosphere. Every year, this mysterious place takes a life. Many chauffeurs who make this journey regularly witness this sad occurrence and believe that this is the dark side of this terrain. People suffer from brain damage and even lose their lives because of the challenges that come with the higher altitude.'

On hearing this, Aanyaa and I are speechless. We don't utter a word till we arrive at the town of Lachen. We will be staying here overnight before resuming our journey for the next four hours.

We are wrapped up in our quilts in Lachen. We get some much-needed sleep. It is a good idea to break up the journey because it is a seven-hour drive through dense forests to Lachen itself. The path is lined with leafy trees, naturally decorating the landscape. The flame of the forest lights up the dense canopy, living up to its name.

On our way up to the army checkpoint, Aanyaa and I had a stopover to relish some authentic delicacies—hot momos and thukpa. Such long journeys by road always make us hungry. We enter a Tibetan lady's tea shop on the side of the never-ending road and occupy the tiny seats inside. We then introduce ourselves to the owner. The tea shop is small yet cosy. We place our order of thukpa with some local tea. Tibetan tea is different; I am glad that Jethi has familiarized us with the local Tibetan cuisines. Because of her strong influence in shaping our characters, we are the perfect mountain dwellers. Tibetan tea has a strong aroma, and butter is a key ingredient. It is a delicacy in the mountains and is meant to fill your body with heat and energy to withstand the harsh climate of the Himalayan belt.

As we enjoy the freshly prepared feast laid out for us, our eyes are also feasting on the view outside, which is out of this world. Wild yaks are grazing below and two riverine streams merge and join, making it appear like a large V-shaped plateau. One of the crystal-clear streams has an emerald green hue while the other is of a turquoise blue shade. The subtle merging of these colourful rivers looks like a masterpiece. It is a picture that is now imprinted on my mind.

Lost in the beauty of the plateau, our excitement for what lies ahead reaches its peak. Finishing our meal, we say thank you to the lady for her hospitality and proceed on our journey.

We finally make it to the Tibetan Plateau. The vast untouched area runs for miles and miles, seemingly never-ending. The terrain shifts from lush and green to rugged and brown within minutes and the cold and dry desert lands lie ahead. Suddenly, the treacherous uphill climb ends and we have the plateau in front of us.

'Extraordinary!' Aanyaa gasps, taking her camera out to capture this moment. Although we have lived in Sikkim and Darjeeling our entire lives, we have yet to fully explore this terrain. Our excitement is off the charts. 'We are at the top of the world,' Aanyaa says, as she enthusiastically holds my hand. I cannot believe my eyes as I see such a different landscape lying in wait for us, right under our noses.

'Who knew such tranquillity existed a few-hour drive from our home? Finally, we have made it to the place that has been on our wish list for ages...among our top ten places to visit in the world, Rea,' Aanyaa adds in a carefree manner.

Our car wheels are running smoothly, now that we are on the Tibetan Plateau. 'Madams, Gurudongmar Lake is one of the last waterbodies that appears on the Indian side of the border,' our chauffeur explains in a loud voice so that we can hear him despite the wind gusting through the lowered windowpanes. 'Madams, a two-hour drive from here lies the border of Tibet, and the Chinese troops are stationed at their line of defence. We are the closest one can get to reaching Tibet,' says the proud chauffeur.

We can now see the waterbody at a distance in a miniature form. There it is! Gurudongmar Lake. 'Rea, it is almost at our arm's reach. The twinkling lake with turquoise waters is ready to welcome us in her divine presence. I wish we had more than twenty minutes to soak in its energy field!'

I can't gaze at the lake without my sunglasses on. There is nothing around but unsullied nature. It is freezing out here and the winds are stronger at the edge of the lake. No words, no photographs, no expressions can capture the sight in front of us.

'Can you see this, Rea? How can this be real? Welcome to Shambhala,' Aanyaa says to me with a satisfied smile.

I am speechless. All I can say is 'Yes. This is real,' and we stand silently for the entire twenty minutes.

35

THE SNOW LIONS

Aanyaa and I have a hobby of collecting beautiful artefacts. This is something our parents instilled in us at a very young age to expand our horizons about ancient cultures of the world. Each holiday would end with us entering antique stores, where my parents' eyes would land on some exquisite pieces, which we would then carefully bring back home. This is a ritual we follow even now, whenever we travel the world.

During our journey to the Kingdom of Bhutan, we spy a beautiful pair of snow lions in Paro. I spot a wooden shop with small stools kept right outside the door. A strong aroma draws me into its curated maze. A statue of a sublime lotus is emitting an alluring scent of lavender.

'Aanyaa, can you smell that? It's so sweet. Come inside with me. Let's take a look,' I say to my sister as we venture into the shop. 'Come have a look at these beautiful snow lions, Rea. I have never seen such craftsmanship before. Do you notice the delicate carvings and radiant colours? Extraordinary, isn't it?' my sister says as she analyses the lions, almost double the size of her palms.

'Aanyaa, I have been fascinated by these beauties for a long time now. Bhutan is the perfect spot to add them to our collection. Snow lions are mythical creatures belonging to our Himalayan belt. They depict strong characteristics of the male and female forms—yin and yang energies—in nature.'

We fall in love with it and decide to add it to our secret room when the shopkeeper says, 'Snow lions are meant to be gifted to someone as a sign of bringing good fortune to the bearer. It mustn't be kept for yourself or it will lose its magical properties. One of you needs to be the gift bearer.' So we glance at each other with a straight face, anticipating as to who would be the recipient among us of these lucky artefacts. Which one of us would make the sacrifice? My stars are looking good and my sister seems to be in a good mood. Or maybe I am pushing it too far. Aanyaa, nevertheless, decides to take the lead. The snow lions are coming with us, one way or another. So she becomes the gift bearer in the end. I am persuasive when I need to be...or maybe it is the pleading look on my face that melts her heart.

The shopkeeper shares captivating legends about snow lions, increasing our curiosity. He says to us from across the flat glass counter, 'Ladies, apart from bestowing good fortune, the snow lions represent the icy glaciers and snow-clad mountains. These beings symbolize happiness, inner and outer strength of the body as well as the mind, valour and power. They depict one of the four key natural elements on the globe—the earth element. Snow lions are revered by the people of Northeast India and Bhutan because they are considered sacred. They have a significant place in Tibetan Buddhism. According to religious texts, the protectors of the Buddha are none other than two sacred snow lions that hold up his heavenly throne. Snow lions are also depicted in ancient scriptures and artwork as the eight guardian lions that represent the eight bodhisattvas in Tibetan Buddhism.'

I am soon lost in this parallel universe. Snow lions have been my guardians for a long time now. I lovingly call them "Guardians of the High Himalayas".

⌒

I have the perfect spot in mind for the two snow lions. They will be in my sacred space, guarding my jade Avalokiteśvara. On my personal altar, there is a Buddhist prayer wheel, a rose quartz and a scented white candle. Aanyaa and I assign the names of Fire and Ice to the snow lions after their attributes. Our yin–yang, male–female snow lions symbolize positivity and purity and bless and protect our Himalayan home.

As we are admiring the eyes of these snow lions, Jethi enters our bedroom. With a bowl of hot milk in hand, she prepares her night ritual.

'Oh, Jethi, where have you been? Look what we brought with us from Bhutan,' my sister says, placing Fire and Ice on Jethi's rough hands. Her palm has strong criss-crossing lines, which tell their own story. Aanyaa glances at the reflection of Jethi's hands in the antique Venetian mirror. 'This world is so beautiful.' Jethi watches in silence as Aanyaa admires Jethi's withered hands against her youthful ones.

'Do you think I am beautiful?' Aanyaa asks us as always.

'Of course you are, and you very well know it. We all know that you are quite the looker in the family. I think you are the only one among us siblings who resembles grandmother. You have her light complexion and sharp features. And you look beautiful with your diamond nose stud, which is exactly like Badi Mama's. Your hazel eyes come from Mama though,' I say, carefully observing my sister.

Suddenly, we hear a faint sound near the window.

'I am ugly.' We hear a familiar voice say, 'I know I am ugly to look at. I accept reality.' Jethi is standing by the window and whispering, 'I know this by the way strangers look at me. Especially foreigners who look at me from top to bottom, giving me the most peculiar stare. "Red Indian! Look, a Red Indian!" Children point at me.' Jethi pushes her salt and pepper hair away from her face. It is an unusual occurrence where Jethi cracks open her hard shell, exposing her vulnerability.

Aanyaa, as quick with her words as she is with her gestures, promptly replies, 'What absolute nonsense! Not at all, Jethi. Who says that you are ugly? You are the cutest person alive. Just look at your adorable face.' Aanyaa gently pulls Jethi's cheeks together to convert her sad frown into a smile. I add, 'You are our very own blanket of comfort and the most beautiful person I know of.'

Aanyaa heads over to the glass cabinet and arrives with just the thing to lighten up the mood. She holds Jethi's hand and discloses a toy. 'You are our magical troll. You remind me of someone with playful energy, a bright pink dress and shimmering silver hair. This pink dress is similar to the bakhu you are wearing, Jethi. Even the twinkling eyes resemble yours. Now don't you tell me that trolls aren't cute. I have an entire collection of them because they are so adorable. They are magical beings just like you, Jethi,' Aanyaa says, caressing Jethi's arms while I watch them.

36

THE TSONGMO LAKE

One of the most visited places in Sikkim, one that attracts individuals from all around the world, is the enchanting Tsongmo Lake. It is located near the dangerous Nathu La Pass, which is the frontier of the Indian army. They have a large permanent base for protecting the Indian borders at high altitudes. Tourists also flock there to see our neighbours at the frontline—the patrolling Chinese troops.

'Aanyaa, come here, quick! I am eager to see our neighbours from across the border. This dividing line is considered one of the main strongholds of the Indian army, protecting a strategic mountain pass that links these powerful nations. Come up quick, soldier on!' I say to my sister as I steadily walk up the numerous stairs towards the border. It's freezing here but I still manage to speak to my sister, even at these heights. My mother calls us both 'Miss Chatterbox' for good reason. We both got this name the day our mother caught us talking for almost twenty-nine hours straight.

'Aanyaa, I must let you in on the history of Nathu La Pass. In ancient times, Nathu La Pass was a part of the silk route, linking India to the Tibetan Plateau where movement of traders on the mighty Himalayan mountains was tough and full of unexpected dangers. On the way up to Nathu La Pass is the mesmerizing Tsongmo Lake.'

We have visited this lake multiple times since we were

children, but with each visit, it grows even more alluring. My father's friend, stationed at the Indian military base, would take us on many trips, exploring these secret mountains. This always used to be a trip with the army generals in military vehicles.

General Brian and his wife Sonia, our dear friends, are stationed here in the northeast. This charming couple are a delight to be around and I have a soft spot in my heart for their daughter Rose. She plays the piano splendidly, striking each chord with such perfection that you won't know she was born without eyesight. Her personality comes across strongly with an intellectual and creative side, one that is also aspirational. Our family takes trips with them and they take us into unknown valleys of the Himalayas, which only the military can access, with a special permit.

'Papa! Have a look at those massive Himalayan yaks in the distance,' I say, tugging at my father's cashmere overcoat. My father shares his knowledge as we explore the terrain, 'The mythical Tsongmo Lake is a naturally occurring lake with snow-clad mountains feeding its waters. The lake is surrounded in all directions by blankets of snow and is home to freely roaming wild yaks. These gigantic creatures are our mountain's inhabitants and live alongside local Tibetan dwellers.'

'Rea, come over here! It's freezing near the edges of the lake. I have something ready to warm you up,' I hear Jethi's voice from a nearby small tea stall. I walk into the tea stall to find a strange smell. 'Here you go. Come enjoy some delicious Tibetan tea. Fresh yak's milk is used to make this special tea. Have a bite of the chhurpi too,' she says while fixing her glasses. Himalayan chhurpi, a kind of cheese prepared with yak milk, provides sustenance to the locals in this harsh landscape. It can last for hours and melts slowly in your mouth. It provides energy and has a strong aftertaste. On a visit to Tsongmo Lake, this delicacy is a must-have.

The high altitudes of Nathu La can leave people unsettled if they have some kind of breathing problem. We brought an oxygen cylinder and the army generals too came prepared. My mother, though accustomed to heights, surprisingly fell short of breath on the stairway up a steep climb.

On closer inspection, there is much more to this lake than having snow fights and enjoying the natural environment. A local legend surrounding Tsongmo Lake leaves me bewildered. Jethi is quick to share a local tale. 'Tsongmo is also known as "the fortune-telling lake". Legend has it that the colour of the lake is said to predict the future of the land. It is believed that if the colour of the lake runs dark, then bad fortune will fall on the local inhabitants, whereas, if the colour is light blue, then good fortune is to arrive on the land. Luckily for us, this day seems to be a good one. The colour of its water is bright blue.'

The glittering lake looks magical. I step on its edge and feel its gentle waves carrying my energy into its vast turquoise surface. A voice in my heart silently speaks to the enchanted lake.

'Hello there, Lady of the Lake! Can you tell me my fortune? What can you see in my destiny?' I say, gazing into its waters to receive its answer.

'Legend claims that once there was a traveller who fell into the ice-cold waters of this lake and never emerged! Jethi adds. 'He was lost somewhere within its strong currents. The fortune-telling lake has gripped the attention of many travellers, not just because of its mesmerizing beauty but also for the legends behind its existence.'

'One of the best-known stories of Sikkim is a story of a supernatural soldier on duty. As one visits Nathu La Pass on the borders of Tibet, it becomes mandatory to pay a visit to the shrine dedicated to the "spirit soldier". A temple has been built on these snow-clad mountains, and it holds photographs, clothes and various belongings of this supernatural soldier. This sacred space is known to the common man as Baba Mandir. The Indian army has built it as a memorial because it is believed that the spirit of the soldier still resides here, protecting the borders of India.'

I am fascinated by the history behind Baba Mandir, so I soldier on towards the army men patrolling the border. I need to uncover the significance of this temple they revere so much. A middle-aged army man offers me a seat in his four-wheeler and starts telling me about the temple. 'Madam, what I'm about to share is a true story. One that should not be taken lightly. This is a very auspicious place for the Indian army. Our sentiments are attached to its history. Long ago, a young soldier named Baba Harbhajan Singh died in an accident, drowning in a gushing stream. The year was 1968. The Indian army went searching for his remains but could not locate them in this rugged landscape, even after going on multiple expeditions. After a few days, Baba Harbhajan Singh miraculously appeared in the dream of a colleague, giving him the location of his body and instructing him to make a shrine, or samadhi, there. On hearing this, a search party was sent out to locate his body immediately. They did find the soldier's body there, which astonished the entire Indian army that was posted at Nathu La Pass.

'In the memory of this soldier, the Indian army created a shrine and kept his belongings in it. The bed is made, his uniform is kept neatly ironed and food is arranged every day at this shrine. As night crawls in, we army men lock the room from the outside and stand guard at its doors till sunrise. When we open the door, all of Babaji's belongings have been used, and the room seems like it has been occupied by a real man. His belongings are scattered everywhere, and the bed is tucked in, as though someone has slept on it the previous night. This sight leaves us speechless, as there is no possible logical explanation for it. It happens on a regular basis and we witness it ourselves. It solidifies our belief; it is nothing but a miracle.'

When I walk into Baba Harbhajan Singh's shrine, there are hundreds of water bottles lined near the gurdwara, the holy place of the Sikhs. I ask the Indian soldier on duty, 'Hello Sir! Why are there so many bottles of water here? Is it a custom of some sort?'

The army man replies, 'The water you see in these jars is considered holy. It is blessed by Babaji himself. Take this holy water to your home and keep it in your mandir. It will bring luck and countless blessings into your home. Babaji visits this shrine every day and blesses these waters himself. We feel his presence here. He protects the borders and gives the army men warning signs if something disastrous is about to occur. Babaji gives us a three-day notice if there is any attack coming from China, and so we are never startled by a surprise encounter. We feel protected in this terrain with the presence of Babaji. He is our guide and our saviour.'

I walk into the shrine, laden with thoughts of the mysterious soldier. I pay my respects and take a bottle of holy water with me back to my home at Nor-Khill, Gangtok.

The mystery behind the blessed water and the presence of the spirit on duty will always stay with me. The army's belief in Baba's supernatural existence is so strong that even a sceptic will have doubts. This protective entity too guards our Indian borders. The spirit on duty! This story is unlike anything I have ever come across in the northeastern Himalayas.

37

VALLEY OF FLOWERS

Yumthang Valley boasts various rare species of flora, which makes it a perfect spot to get lost in. During the months of April and early May, as spring enters Yumthang Valley (or the 'valley of flowers'), we celebrate the end of the harsh winter months of ice and snow. Situated at a distance of 130 kilometres from Gangtok at an altitude of 11,693 feet above mean sea level, this valley is a holy grail for nature lovers. Himalayan yaks graze in tranquillity and wild horses run freely through this breathtaking natural wonderland. Sitting on lush Himalayan grass, admiring the multicoloured meadows and just feeling the essence of untouched natural beauty is every person's dream come true.

I go to the Valley of Flowers with my sister. Not many have an adventurous streak in them like we do. I gaze at Aanyaa's lilac shawl and feel an unusual sensation surround me at that very moment.

'Aanyaa, do you feel a little strange too? I am feeling weightless, like a cloud.' I lie down on the grass between the exotic flowers.

My sister giggles and says, 'The flowers in the Yumthang Valley have the extraordinary ability to intoxicate people with their scent. There are so many different species of flowers here that all of them combined light up your innermost senses. Unlike any other Himalayan terrain, Yumthang has flora and fauna that is unique.'

I lie down on the valley of flowers when a memory makes me hold onto my sister tightly as I say, 'Aanyaa, do you remember the time I grabbed your arm in my dream only to wake up and do the same in real life? It was a vision I had of you! I remember there were flowers all around my room that day. My bedroom smelled just like this. I had arrived from the nursery with a handful of flowers—primulas—to keep on my bedside table. I went to bed that night, smelling their sweet scent, only to wake with a sudden jerk. Was it a bad dream? I had to be certain! Do you recall that moment, Aanyaa?'

My sister surely knows what I am referring to. 'I had a dream of you trying to please the Goddess by going on a sudden hunger strike. You pledged not to eat even a single grain of rice till your prayer was heard. I saw Goddess Kali in a rage asking me to stop you immediately. Her eyes were flaring with anger. Imagine Goddess Kali in a rage! How frightening that can be. I woke up suddenly from my dream and called you that very moment to find out that my dream had been a vision. It was around 2 a.m., way past midnight. I stopped you just in time before you commenced your hunger strike. I couldn't believe it. We both were absolutely stunned!'

My sister falls silent for a while and then, finally, opens up. 'I wonder if this runs in the family, Rea? This gift of vision. It keeps me wondering if such things can be genetic. Mama, Viraj, you and I have all individually felt and seen things happen before they actually occur. I recall a moment when I had a vivid vision of Pitaji, our grandfather. Mama was on the phone with her brother, planning her next visit home to Delhi. She was on the verge of delaying her trip by a week when I interrupted her conversation and said, "Mama, go to

Delhi tomorrow. I think you should go as soon as possible!"
Little did I know that Pitaji would suddenly pass away, only
two days later. Mama and I were startled by this, leaving us
in absolute silence.'

Aanyaa and I drift into the valley of flowers to connect
to the Devi, the Goddess in the wild landscape. I have never
witnessed miles and miles of rhododendrons blooming like
I have in Yumthang. Countless species of rhododendrons
bloom, with colours ranging from fuchsia to purple to pure
white. Usually, the Himalayas are laden with bright crimson
rhododendrons, but in Yumthang, there is a spectrum of
colours. This is home to the Shingba Rhododendron Sanctuary,
where they have a collection of 40 species of this Himalayan
flower. Yumthang also hosts cobra lilies, poppies, primroses,
saxifrages, primulas and cinquefoils—all have an intoxicating
smell in full bloom.

'Rea, how can I forget? Do you remember what happened
with Viraj? His connection with Badi Mama, our grandmother,
was so strong that he once had a clear vision of her. I recall
that Viraj was studying in Switzerland, far away from home.
But he felt the Himalayas calling out to him while in the Swiss
Alps. He woke up from his sleep to call home and speak to
Mama. In the dead of night, Viraj said, "Mama, I could not be
there for Grandmother's funeral but I have attended it in my
vision. I saw the entire ceremony in my dream this morning
while it was taking place there. I saw Badi Mama taking my
hand and blessing me. I saw the wood and fire go off by the
banks of the Teesta. The funeral was on the riverbank, wasn't
it?" Mama was left shocked on the phone and said, "Yes, Viraj.
It was by the river. Badi Mama has connected with you. She
wanted her favourite grandson to be at her funeral. God bless
her, and may God bless you, my son."'

Aanyaa and I have tears in our eyes; we are overwhelmed by emotion. But soon we start to relax among the flowers, appreciating the nature surrounding us. It's a paradise! A surreal walk into the mythical Elysian fields. This valley is said to be the last point where trees grow as the land beyond is covered with snow-capped hills and icy glaciers.

'Come, Rea, we surely have had a long day enjoying the scenic beauty. The best part still awaits us—the natural hot springs of Yumthang Valley, which is the most relaxing part of this trip.' My sister picks up some rock salt and guides my way. The rich sulphur content in the water mixed with Himalayan salts is known for its unique healing abilities. A dip into these natural hot springs not only removes ailments from the body but also relaxes the mind as well.

'Rea, I must tell you a tale of two sisters.' I am drawn to her words and say, 'Yes, go on. I am all ears.'

'My story is about Mama and her elder sister, which I heard from Mama only. They were engrossed in a conversation about the misfortunes occurring in the latter's life. Our Maasi was upset and agitated by the strange accidents around the new house. Mama went to bed that night, only to get the answer she was looking for in a vision. She called her sister immediately. Maasi, who lives in South Africa, was asked one simple question. She said, "Deshi, do you live in a house placed between three corners?" Maasi was stunned by Mama's sudden question and said, "Yes, Nimmi! Our new house is shaped in that exact way! How did you know this? You have never even seen the house!" Mama said, "Deshi, I want you to shift out of it as soon as possible. I had a dream that you were locked inside a three-cornered house with no doors or windows. No escape in sight. I have a feeling your house has heavy energies inside it. The three corners create a negative vibration within its dimensions." Can you believe it, Rea?'

Gazing at the white Kanchenjunga, I hold my sister's hand and feel magic flow through us. These healing waters are a one-of-a-kind Himalayan wilderness spa. The Yumthang Valley of Flowers cannot be described in words, it can only be experienced. It is our Elysium on Earth.

38

THE NAKED TREE

In the small town of Kalimpong, there is a spectacular sight. Only people who have seen it believe in its existence. It is said that unknown sightings of mysterious flying objects are frequent in these vast Himalayan ranges. Unidentified aerial discs are spotted on some clear nights by the local inhabitants. Is this myth or reality? That is up to the spectators. I have heard of a first-hand account of such an encounter in the premises of The Elgin Silver Oaks, our third home. My mother and Aanyaa have been witnesses to this extraordinary sighting.

One October morning, I am listening in on Aanyaa and Mama discussing something unreal. The ladies are so engrossed in their conversation that they barely notice me leaning on the door of the Oak lounge. I suddenly hear the word 'alien'. Both of them sport pale faces, as if they have seen a ghost. Because ghostly encounters are not unusual in the hills, I think there is something else they have stumbled upon. As I make my way towards the lounge, I trip and fall flat on my face, making a huge noise. My mother and sister turn around to see me picking myself up from the wooden floor and laughing my heart out.

It has been a childhood habit of mine to burst into laughter each time I have had a fall, hurt myself or was caught doing something I shouldn't have been doing. 'What is the matter, Mama? I can see something intense is going on here. I too want to be a part of the conversation.'

My mother gives a blank look to Aanyaa. Hesitant at first, she allows me to participate. I quickly order a hot apple juice with cinnamon and sit on the high-back chair. 'Well, Rea, you will not believe what we witnessed last night,' Aanyaa says, all excited. 'I have been dying to spill the beans, but Mama asked me to keep my lips sealed.'

I am even more interested. 'Come on, tell me what happened. I already heard you mention alien,' I say, placing my legs on the couch. My mother instantly puts her hand over her mouth, covering it, caught in a dilemma.

'Were we that loud, Rea? I thought I was being as quiet as a mouse,' she says, disappointed. 'Well, I guess not,' I reply confidently.

My mother had no other option now but to tell me the story in detail. The cat was halfway out of the bag. I was not going to move off the couch without hearing the whole story. 'Rea, sit down and stop firing questions at me. What I am about to tell you is not to be taken lightly. There are a lot of guests around. The hotel's occupancy is full this week. So do not go about with a loudspeaker repeating what I am about to tell you. The guests will be startled, and some may even be terrified. They might just go back to their homes.'

I give her my word that I will not tell a soul what I was about to hear. So my mother begins her tale, a hint of hesitation in her voice. She is clearly sceptical.

'Last night, Aanyaa and I were sitting on the bench outside, gazing at the stars. It was a clear cloudless sky and we had a good view of the astral bodies. I was pointing out Orion's belt among the glittering expanse when, to my surprise, I witnessed a strange spherical object flying high up in the sky. It was moving slowly at first, then it suddenly picked up momentum. The object started moving left, then right, then left again. It kept changing its direction, unlike any aeroplane or helicopter I have seen.'

'We thought at first that it may be a shooting star or even an asteroid. Or an army helicopter. My mind was trying to make sense of the object. It did not seem like anything I could identify. All of a sudden, the spherical object began to emit bright navy blue light from its surface, even as it constantly changed its position. I could not take my eyes off the object, and then it did something absolutely baffling. A laser-like beam from the mysterious flying object seemed to target something in the forest. Within a few seconds, another beam pointed in the same direction. My eyes were glued to the mysterious machine till it vanished into the dark sky. The entire experience lasted for about ten to fifteen minutes. I clutched onto Aanyaa tightly, and for a moment, I was left speechless. I went to bed quietly, taking a hot water bottle with me for comfort. I couldn't say a word and I'm sure Diamond was amazed by my silence the entire night. Today, in the early hours of the morning, when the sun began to rise, I quickly went to the window and noticed a gigantic coniferous tree had turned absolutely dry. Its branches were broken, and no leaves were in sight. The tree stood alone, stripped of its greenery, among the hundreds of lush trees surrounding it. I am still in shock. What if what we encountered was more than a naked tree? Could it be an alien spaceship? My mind started asking countless questions. Were we visited by intelligent alien life last night?' my mother asks, bewildered.

This incident remains a mystery for us. We might never know for certain what that object actually was, but my mother is convinced that it was something out of this world.

The following night, my elder brother, Viraj, is watching his favourite show *The X-Files*, which deals with alien encounters. He is really interested in science and technology, and his favourite pastime includes reading up on a variety of subjects that are either extinct or alien, such as prehistoric dinosaurs and artificial intelligence. He is watching an interesting episode. It shows aliens abducting humans to experiment on them. The vivid graphics on the screen spook the living daylights out of Viraj. As soon as he sees a man being abducted in his sleep by an unknown object, Viraj runs into Aanyaa and my room, gripping his pillow tightly.

'I am sleeping here tonight!' Viraj says, his glasses askew. Aanyaa, ever the mischief maker, tells him about her and Mama's 'real alien encounter' in the oak garden last night.

'Are you joking? Rea, she is fooling around, isn't she?' Viraj stands by the door, contemplating what to do next.

'Rea won't lie. Rea will tell you what "really" happened,' Aanyaa says with glee.

'Yes, it is true. Why don't you ask Mama about it?

My brother is so terrified after this that he sleeps right in between us. He says, 'If aliens come for us tonight, they have a choice of three individuals to abduct. I can take my chances. They may go for people sleeping on either side and may leave the man in the middle.'

Viraj thinks he would be abducted in his sleep too. As for me, the only time I have seen aliens is when my father took me on my first trip to Paris. I was eleven years old when Papa gave me a clear warning. Papa, right there at the airport, told me in a serious voice, 'Look, Rea, we are in an alien country. This is my briefcase where all our money and passports are. You have to keep an eye on it or we will have a tough time getting home.'

I took my father's words very seriously and decided to

protect the briefcase at all costs. I found just the way to do it. Wherever we went, I would sit on the briefcase. Finally, when the trip was over, I asked Papa a very serious question. 'Papa, I need to ask you something. During our entire trip, I did not see even one alien. Where are the aliens?' Viraj, Aanyaa and I share a hearty laugh at the memory, yet we sleep with the bedside lamp on, just in case.

39

EARLY CONVERSATIONS WITH THE MOUNTAIN GOD

'It's 8 a.m. Out of bed! Let's go. Girls, pack your suitcase for the weekend.'

We twist around in bed, not letting go of our hot water bottles, when suddenly, someone pulls off our fluffy blanket. My mother shakes us out of our warm den.

'It's Friday.'

'Are we going on a surprise vacation?' my sister asks.

'Oh yes, we are,' I murmur and rush towards the bathroom and the hot tub that I am sure our housekeeper Chanda has kept ready for us. Now my sister has to wait for her turn or resort to a hot water shower instead.

'You mischievous little brat!' yells my mother from afar. I love starting my day with a green apple-scented bubble bath. Also, I already know we are off on a road trip. My parents had been planning a trip to Sikkim the whole week. I kept it a secret, not disclosing and ruining the surprise for Aanyaa. Road trips mean riverside picnics and I can't wait to get my hands on the picnic basket.

'We are going to Pemayangtse. The weather is going to be cold up there, so put on your knitted woollens and grab your pashmina shawls too.' I love the smell and softness of pashmina. It is very comforting, especially when outdoors.

'We have to show you a new property. You girls will love it. Your brother is up and about already. Viraj cannot contain his excitement and is waiting for us there,' my mother says with enthusiasm while trying to get my sister to drink a glass of milk containing Himalayan honey and a pinch of haldi. It is our Mama's 'natural detoxification' method. Childhood habits seldom go away, especially when you have an Indian mother. No matter our age, we will always be their 'kids'.

The road to Sikkim is the most picturesque, as valleys of flowers greet us along the state borders. Dainty violet wildflowers merge with rosette and mint-green hues on the hillside, providing a scene of tranquillity. I feel a sudden urge to roll down these violet fields and be one with the lush meadows and let my imagination run wild. The best part still lies on the other side of the suspended bridge connecting the two states of West Bengal and Sikkim, as the zigzagging roads make their way into a blanket of clouds.

The single-lane Himalayan road seems to be floating above the fluffy white clouds. It almost feels like we are flying. This feeling is truly magical and unreal. Little did I know that our destination ahead is to be even more splendid than the scenic journey we are on, as the smell of cardamom engulfs the mountains with miles and miles of forests.

We finally enter Pemayangtse. A black rustic gate decorated with roaring dragons welcomes us to our new home. Our fourth home, The Elgin Mount Pandim, used to be the summer palace of the royal family of Sikkim. It appears to be a fortress built on top of a mountain with a 360-degree view of the entire town below. The Kanchenjunga range in the Himalayas acts as a natural barricade, keeping the area hidden from the world.

But the range could not hide this treasure from the man who is perpetually drawn to these historic sights—Mr

Diamond. My father has a sharp eye for heritage properties. Anything over a hundred years old is his favourite pick. He is a builder and a protector in the true sense of the word. Mr Diamond likes to build from scratch, and his intricate work is reflected in his heritage hotels. 'This is my medium of expression, connecting with people from diverse backgrounds, giving back to society and surrounding myself with exquisite nature at all times.'

Mr Diamond's love for historic sites is unparalleled, as are his storytelling abilities. My father goes on to tell us the history of this royal summer palace and why he chose to make it a part of The Elgin group. Holding a snifter of brandy with a dash of Himalayan honey in his hands, my father says, 'My lovely ladies have ventured into a place crawling with history. The summer palace of Mount Pandim was only used by the royal family and their personal guests. This was a special retreat of the Chogyal, the monarchs of the former Kingdom of Sikkim, because the holy monastery of Pemayangtse opposite this summer palace was used for the coronation ceremony of the Chogyal himself. The old capital of Sikkim was located near the town of Pemayangtse, and thus this place was considered one of the greatest strongholds of the kingdom and was beloved by the kings. There are accounts of the late Chogyal sitting on this garden's wooden bench and looking at the holy peak of Mount Pandim for hours, painting the marvellous peaks on canvas. This was one of the royals' favourite spots to unwind from their busy schedules and take solace in prayer and serenity of these holy mountains. This hotel was named after a peak called Mount Pandim, which is a part of the guardian deity of Sikkim—the Khangchendzonga. The Kanchenjunga mountain is sacred for the local Lepcha, Limbu and Bhutia tribes. It is an abode of the Gods. Do you know the Lepchas are the oldest tribe in Sikkim? They believe that their first master, Azaor Boongthing, was created from the purest snowflake of Mount Pandim by the God Aitbu Deburoom. The Lepchas tell tales of a hidden utopia, a paradise somewhere in the foothills of the Kanchenjunga range. Tibetans believe the Kanchenjunga to be the gateway to Shambhala—a mythical land of ascended masters and immortal beings.'

The next morning, with the rising sun, the splendour of nature rises alongside us. 'It's 5 a.m. Get off the bed quickly... magic awaits you,' my mother says, drawing back the curtains excitedly. Rubbing our eyes and adjusting them to the bright sunlight coming in through the French windows, Aanyaa and I enjoy the view of the mighty Mount Pandim.

It seems as if I could just stretch my arms and grab the mountains, which are glowing with orange and golden hues of sunlight falling gently on their white peaks. It looks absolutely blissful. The light from the heavens illuminates the top of the peak as it slowly makes its way down to the entire mountain range, turning it violet.

'Look at nature welcoming you to your new home,' my mother says. 'What does the range remind you of, girls?' Aanyaa and I tap into our artistic side to figure out the form in which the mountain range appears to us. 'I do not know,' we say out loud together.

'Look closely!' Mama says. My father walks into our room from the corridors in his long velvet night robe, giving us a good morning hug and kisses on our forehead.

'The sleeping Buddha,' my father whispers into our ears. His answer ends the curiosity my mother has been building in our minds all this while. 'You girls seem all set this morning. Wow, look at that sight. Isn't it marvellous? The mountain range appears to be in the form of a reclining Buddha.'

My father takes us downstairs to the garden where a large telescope has been set up facing the Himalayan range. 'Come and take a closer look. Focus on the tallest peak. There…at the centre, called Mount Pandim. This view is one of a kind,' Mr Diamond says, pointing his finger at the peak.

As I peep into the metal frame, there it is… The crystal-clear view of the reclining Buddha in all its glory. The peak of Mount Pandim at the centre of the range creates an image of the Buddha, with the smaller peaks creating his head on the left, stretching all the way to the tiny peaks towards the right, which look just like his feet. 'Wow Papa! I can see it so clearly. This is so breathtaking,' I exclaim, jumping barefoot on the moist grass. 'Move over, Rea. It's my turn now. Let me see.' My sister looks through the telescope and begins to survey the serene mountains.

The sight is extraordinary. The sky is a canvas brimming with gradually shifting hues of the morning sun, from coral to fuchsia pink and lilac. Far away, the pearly white Kanchenjunga stands straight, with a majestic aura around it, like an emperor in all its glory. My father, tuning in to his spiritual self, says, 'My darlings, we are truly blessed to have been given this opportunity to witness the reclining Buddha from the comfort of our new home. Devotees, mountaineers and pilgrims set off on arduous journeys from all around the globe to come here, just to glance at this sacred mountain. Close your eyes for a minute and connect with the reclining Buddha. You may hear its divine voice speaking to you. Let the magic of the land be your guide.' My father does the same and we follow in his footsteps. To open my heart to the cosmos and its natural wonders is what I have learnt to do from the very beginning. Spending time with nature is a form of meditation that is vital for our minds. These mountains of West Sikkim have become my place of worship. No man-made structure can come close to nature's divine auric field, especially that of the Himalayas. It is unlimited, untamed and undivided.

Sikkim is shrouded in mysticism. Aanyaa and I continue our quest for spiritual knowledge as we find ourselves in the company of a mystic. As we relish hot sweet corn soup in Kanchen Garden, the mystic—dressed in pure white from head to toe, with wooden slippers—takes us on a journey into Pemayangtse's wild woods. This learned man shifts his gaze towards the holy monastery's grounds of Pemayangtse and says, 'Yogic culture points to a deep understanding of the human mind and body. Just like our physical body has energy points known as chakras, the earth too has its distinct energy points. Sikkim is divided from north to south into four energy centres, one of which is the heart chakra. It is one of the most sacred places in the mountain kingdom—the Pemayangtse Monastery in Pelling—right opposite us. This monastery is special, as it is home to rare scriptures. The lamas residing here can trace their ancestry to hundreds of years. This monastery may seem like any other Buddhist monastery at first glance, but it is separated by discreet traditions.'

I see my sister absorbing it all in. The Elgin Mount Pandim is located at a ten-minute brisk walk from this monastery.

On our visits to Pelling, our mornings start with my parents taking us for an uphill walk through a serene pathway decorated with white Buddhist prayer flags as we move towards the holy grounds of the monastery. As we walk past the driveway in the winter months, flaming red flowers of salvia and poinsettias welcome us into the king's summer palace— now our home. We walk past a mystical stupa built right at the entrance of the hotel and the holy monastery. It serves as a landmark to find our way home, no matter how dark it gets in the thick of the forest. Himalayan winds brush past us and suddenly, we feel the presence of someone else. A Himalayan barking deer strolls through the silent forest.

'Look at this magnificent beauty. What a sighting we have had today. The forest is home to these Himalayan deer. So technically, we are in their territory. Nimmi, move away without startling this gentle creature. Please be quiet and quick,' my father says.

My mother takes the lead and guides us through the forest as we slowly move away from the deer. 'Aanyaa, Rea, listen carefully. The history of this monastery is steeped in ancient legends. It is believed to have been built over a serene lotus structure,' my mother whispers to us in the cold. 'As per legend, a large lotus miraculously appeared from the heavens as a blessing from the Gods, and the structure of this monastery took its shape from that lotus. Thus, this place got its name Pemayangtse, meaning "The Perfect Sublime Lotus". Mama builds up the mystery as we get closer to the gates of the monastery. 'A lotus signifies various stages of enlightenment in Buddhism. It blossoms in murky waters, giving way to a pure heart. Guru Padmasambhava, the central figure in Tibetan Buddhism, is said to be born out of a lotus, emerging from its delicate petals. These mountains have tales of Gautama Buddha spreading blooming lotuses with every step he took on the land, emerging from the tree of enlightenment. It is a flower of moksha.' My mother's voice enchants us as we observe the large maroon pillars crafted with dragons and snow lions, all of whom are protectors of this holy land.

My father says, 'My dears, this is one of the oldest monasteries in Sikkim, built during the seventeenth century by Lama Lhatsun Chempo. Tibetan Buddhism is divided into many sects and these sects follow different orders of practice. Buddhists strongly believe in the ideology of karma and reincarnation. The third Chogyal of Sikkim was believed to be the reincarnation of the lama who built this monastery. Reincarnation in Tibetan Buddhism means "the one who is born again to complete his unfinished duties in the world". Reincarnates remember their previous births and can give a detailed description of their past life, which is then witnessed by many followers. The monks living here are different from those in other monasteries found in the Himalayas. The lamas of Pemayangtse are considered to be pure monks.'

I ask my father what he means by pure.

He adds, 'When I say "pure lamas" it means that these monks choose to be celibate, untouched by the material world and depict no abnormality of the physical nature. These monks are of a pure lineage, making them entitled to hold the grand title of "ta-tshang".'

I am even more eager to explore the deeper layers of the temple grounds. I want to discover all the fascinating things within this ancient monastery tucked away in Sikkim. I am sure I would find something extraordinary as the older the architecture of the place, the more secrets there are waiting to be discovered.

We enter the monastery, strolling through the grounds, looking at each detail as if we have a magnifying glass in our retinas. My father keeps narrating many historical legends behind the details. 'The kings held this monastery very close to their heart as it was connected to the beginning of their reign. The head lama of Pemayangtse alone had the special privilege of anointing the King of Sikkim with holy water. The monarchy had deep roots in Pemayangtse, and it is revered as one the most important and holy places in Sikkim till this day.'

Exploring the ancient structure, we end up at the very

top. A cosy wooden room twinkled with butter lamps and lit sandalwood incense sticks. A strong buttery smell envelops me as I walk into the attic; a painting of the Buddhist saint, Guru Rimpoche, adorns a wall, the likes of which I have never seen before. The maroon walls also have thankas of mandalas with Buddhist teachings. I then notice a few frames beyond my arm's reach; they are covered with a red cloth. I wonder what they are. They have been kept a secret through the generations and some things are best if they stay like that. I shift my gaze from the maroon walls and let the monastery's energy guide me.

I stumble upon a fascinating man-made structure, a seven-tier wooden manifestation of Guru Rimpoche's heavenly abode, known as the 'Sangthokpalri'. I observe its vivid colours and notice the beautiful description of the lokas, the realms and various stages of the afterlife explained through detailed artwork. There is a clear description of the various realms in which the Gods and astral beings reside. It is designed with an array of rainbows and shows colourful scenes from the lives of various Buddhas and bodhisattvas residing in their heavenly palace. This ancient masterpiece is kept inside a glass display so that no one comes in physical contact with it. The structure stretches upwards from the bottom of the wooden floor—almost touching the ceiling of the attic; it cannot be missed when you come to Pemayangtse Monastery.

My father follows me while I admire the artwork. He says, 'I will bring you to this monastery again when the lamas perform their religious festivals, called the "Cham dance". It is a magnificent sight. The performers wear colourful costumes and the snow lions perform their astral dance. People from all across the land gather here every year for a two-day grand celebration on the 28th and 29th of the twelfth month in the lunar Buddhist calendar.' It is a celebration that my father has enjoyed on his travels here before he took over the Chogyal's summer palace to make it a part of The Elgin. My next visit will surely be during the celestial celebrations to witness this peaceful monastery turn into a vibrant festival ground.

40

GOOSEBUMPS: TALES OF THE LAND

The misty Himalayan mountains are known for their hair-raising ghostly encounters. Horror and excitement transpire at every turn into these silent woods, with local sightings of strange entities and lost souls stuck between realms.

This land grows ethereal with the onset of mist covering the hills and deep woods as the crimson sun starts setting. The darkness holds mystery and inspires folklore. The ghosts of this hill station are very different from those of other places—unique and active, even though the human population is comparatively lower than that in the concrete city jungles. It is often speculated that the hills provide space for every creature's existence, be it humans, animals, trees or the supernatural. Everything has its place and its unique bond with the earth. Tales of the Himalayan land will have you calling for more...

THE JOGI

On a dark moonless night, the curved roads of Darjeeling witness the presence of a mysterious man, and a strange sound echoes throughout the misty town. When the old clock tower strikes midnight, the howling winds accompany the arrival of the jogi. It brings forth a haunted feeling during Amavasya—the darkest night—when the veil separating us from the spirit realm is at its thinnest. It is also known as 'kaal ratri' in Indian mythology.

The month of March is here, and I can hear the unpredictable winds carrying a loud sound through the deep mountains. The lamps are flickering in the dark night and the dogs are howling into the starry sky. The sounds make me want to tuck myself under the bedcovers, yet leave me wanting to uncover the secrets to this mysterious tune. The sky is pitch black, with not even a shadow on the ground. The continuing sound raises everyone's goosebumps, whoever is awake and is hearing it at these odd hours. A sound that cannot be missed, even by someone who is not paying attention. Night owls beware! Come nightfall, the clock turns its gaze. The jogis, known as the disciples of Lord Shiva in Hinduism, carry out an ancient tradition to this modern day in the northeastern Himalayas. The jogis belong to a Nepalese tribe, revered for their spiritual practices, called 'Goraknath'. Hinduism is one of the oldest religions in the world, and its spiritual practices date back centuries. This tribe has a deep-rooted connection with Nepal, Sikkim and Darjeeling, and with the generations who live in these Himalayan mountains. The jogi walks into town alone at midnight, armed with a long horn made from an animal of the deer family called 'brat'. They blow the horn for long stretches of time as they make their rounds around town, covering the entire area.

My mother says, 'It is believed that the earth is inhabited by countless spirits. Some are evil spirits that cause harm to mankind and disturb the natural order of life. In ancient texts, Lord Shiva sent the jogis to perform an important task—to lure evil spirits away from the human world. The jogis chant powerful mantras and blow their horns to lure evil spirits away with them. It is believed that these spirits follow the shankha dhwani like a magnet. Legend has it that one should never look at the jogi while they perform their rituals as this may divert the evil spirits towards us instead, which would be an absolute nightmare.'

As the jogi passes through the lone streets, I can clearly hear his distinct sound in the pin-drop silence of the witching hour, but I quickly close my thick velvet curtains so that even my bedside light is not visible from outside. I hide, which is something that I do when I do not wish to be curious about things that usually come back to bite me.

My mother wakes up instantly, hearing the jogi's call, as she believes they can drive away any negative energy surrounding us. She cleanses her energy with her devi mantra, getting rid of her low vibrations, alongside the jogi's chants and comes to my and Aanyaa's rooms to ensure that we too hear their call in the dead of the night. The Himalayan mountains have a strong connection with the world beyond the veil. It is evident in the culture and livelihood of the people living here, even in this fast-paced technological era. The Himalayan jogi is our very own mystical 'Pied Piper of the town'.

As the darkest night of Amavasya begins to remove its thick blanket from the sky, Lady Dawn brings a new beginning into our little hamlet. My mother is just finishing her yoga routine by welcoming the first rays of the sun with a Surya namaskar at 5 a.m. I can see the jogi from afar, asking for alms or dhaan, going from door to door—a practice carried out through generations. We give them fruits, food, milk or money as a sign of gratitude for his services. The jogi takes what is offered to them calmly and carries on with his daily task. It is the only time when one can look at the jogi's face, without worrying about safety, against the bright sunlight. Dressed in a deep red robe with black trousers, the jogi holds a small woven basket in his hand, filled with leaves and brown prayer beads. His forehead is adorned with a red 'tika' and sprinkled with raw rice grains at the centre.

The Himalayan jogi is always roaming around in our vicinity. This mystical tradition is a constant in the upper Himalayas, inspiring awe in the minds of many people. It baffles the logical mind. Religion, tradition, culture and faith combine to form an essential part of our modern age, blending like a fabric made from two or more fibres, thereby creating something magical in nature. This is the legend of the jogis.

If we hear the jogi's call at midnight, we know that the spiritual Pied Piper is busy with his cleansing rounds. All we have to do then is keep our eyes closed and our ears open so that we can release our low vibrations, which will be taken away by this mystical man into the unknown.

CHILDREN OF THE NIGHT

Dusk is about to set in and the town of Pemayangtse is lighting up with the cold moon upon us. My father is ready to take his evening walk through the canopy of untouched forests surrounding us. This time of dusk is particularly his favourite as the crowds begin to disappear and the wild forest is calm, with no unwanted human interference. Just silence and serenity. It is his time to reflect on the busy day and to be lost in nature's solace. My father lovingly calls it 'forest therapy', an ancient method of natural rejuvenation. Further, the Himalayan winds are a natural cleanser. Cleansing with the wind or a 'wind bath' is a spiritual concept—a technique used to clear the mind and spirit. Mr Diamond's nature walks are usually incomplete without his two guardians, our beloved but overprotective Russian Samoyeds, Coco and Kara, who are Peter and Lilian's siblings, stationed in The Elgin Mount Pandim, Pelling.

But one particular evening was different, when my father went on a walk alone. Off went Mr Diamond through the dragon gates towards the holy lake, all the way to the town of upper Pelling, which is his little paradise. Somewhere during his walk, he came across something hidden away in his sacred space. This evening was marked by an unusual event that left him wondering for days on end. Maybe even for weeks. So much so, that he shares his experience with his friends and guests staying at the hotel and leaves them in wonderment and absolute awe.

With bright charcoal eyes, my father lifts his glasses from his nose and begins his tale while sitting on a couch.

'It was almost seven on my watch. Twilight was upon me with the sky turning amber then reddish plum. I was walking down the lone road, admiring the beauty of Pemayangtse and the towering snow-capped Kanchenjunga range, when I heard a soft voice. The voice of a little boy behind me wearing nothing but a tiny sweater. With a red nose and red eyes, the boy said, "Hello sir, good evening." The little boy giggled slightly. He looked about six years old. "Oh, hello there. Where are you off to all by yourself? I don't see your parents with you," I said, concerned about the boy. "I am going home to my village," replied the little boy, hopping next to me, trying to match my pace, his tiny legs speeding up with my long stride. "Come walk with me. It is getting dark. You are a brave little boy to be walking alone through the forest at this hour." The boy and I kept walking and talking when I noticed something fishy in the little boy's pocket.'

'"Oh! What do you have there?" I asked in a gentle voice. The little boy put his hand into his pocket when suddenly, a tiny goldfish jumped out onto the dry road. The little boy quickly grabbed the fish and put it back into its container. "I went for a picnic with my friends and collected them from a nearby pond. I have an aquarium at home where I am going to keep them. They are my friends now." The little boy said with excitement. Goldfish were swimming in a little plastic carry bag half filled with water. I was surprised as to where he would have found fish in the high mountains of Pemayangtse. The holy lake is a few minutes away but no one touches the water as it is considered sacred and is now a watering hole for wild animals in these jungles. The little boy showed me the tiny goldfish. "Oh, how wonderful! I love fish too. I have a beautiful pond of my own at the hotel!" I said, walking right next to the little boy who barely reached my thigh. "Sir, you should not walk on this main road and take the small pathway I am walking on. Some people drink and drive rashly on this road at this hour." I was amazed by this little boy's intelligence and stepped onto the sidewalk while continuing my stroll. To my astonishment, within a few minutes, a speeding car came towards me and took a very sharp turn ahead. Loud screeches of the tyres echoed in the silent forest, making me uncomfortable. My attention turned towards the speeding car while I was still talking to this little boy. I suddenly looked towards my left to notice that he wasn't there anymore. It had barely been a minute since the boy had been speaking to me. The lone road showed no sign of the little boy. I could clearly see the curved roads stretching far behind and in front of me. Dry twigs, fallen leaves and the open wilderness surrounded me. But there was no sign of any houses or villages nearby, just the dense forest on both sides of the lonely road. Where did the boy go? How could he have just vanished?'

'The moon floated on a cloudless sky. There was nothing but silence. I knew something was surely unusual. A cold Himalayan wind gusted against me, and I called out to the boy in case he had wandered into the forest, but my voice echoed back through the dark canopy of trees. The evening was getting mysterious. *How can this be possible?* I paused for a few minutes and made my way back up the slope to the hotel. This time, I kept looking back in case the little boy showed up, but he didn't. I let out a sigh of relief as I saw the large stupa outside our gates. The sun was setting and the forest was turning darker by the minute. As I walked into the hotel, Coco and Kara started howling at the moon. Lost in thought, I walked into the lobby and sat down on a velvet pouffe in front of the cosy fireplace. I did not say a word for a couple of minutes, the thoughts of the mysterious little boy swimming in my mind. I ordered a hot brandy with honey and composed myself first. Meanwhile, Nimmi came from the royal gardens and noticed that I looked quite startled. "Nimmi, Rea! Come here... Let me tell you what I just encountered on my walk. I am absolutely amazed." Removing my cashmere overcoat and leather gloves, I settle down by the dancing flames, as my father begins his story—a series of supernatural encounters under the celestial moonlight.

THE BISHOP'S ROAD

On a regular basis, we take a picturesque walk through a beautiful, breezy lane with tall oak trees on both sides. It is our shortcut through the bishop's house in Darjeeling to avoid crowds at the busy bazaar. This curvy uphill road leads straight to the back gates of The Elgin. I thoroughly enjoy taking this path and spend many mornings strolling up and down beneath the canopy of coniferous trees. The road, peaceful by day, changes drastically as dusk approaches. With the dimming of natural light, Bishop's Road holds unsolved mysteries, which I have witnessed myself.

One evening, my friend Praj and I got tied up with activities at the convent and left the grounds at about 6.30 p.m. The night was beginning to crawl in early, with the moon already shining overhead. I watched the sun and moon together in the October sky, much like an astral waltz of these heavenly bodies. Tints of ever-changing violet, shell pink and tangerine brightened up the evening sky.

'It's time to head home, Rea. It's beginning to get dark and my stomach is growling. We don't even have a torchlight on us,' Praj said, beginning to pick up her bag and grey overcoat. We left the convent and headed straight for the steps that led up to Bishop's Road. With heavy books on our backs, we climbed slowly, pacing ourselves while catching our breath after a very long day. Chattering away, we walked hand in hand with the strong winds sweeping through our hair. With not a single soul in sight, we matched our steps, ambling through the forest. This evening quietude is a part of our daily lives in the hills and it is nowhere close enough to spook us. We walk this pathway every day confidently and with a carefree attitude.

'This time of the day, with the ever-changing and vibrant sky, is my favourite. Look up at the different colours. How it slowly turns dark,' I whisper to Praj. The lonely road looked hauntingly beautiful as the sky turned dark.

Ten minutes into our walk, we heard something strange behind us. We did not pay attention to it and continued on our path. All of a sudden, I heard a whisper from behind.

'Rea. Rea.'

Someone had called my name. I thought it might be a friend of mine. As I was about to turn around, Praj caught hold of my hand and said, 'Rea, don't turn around. I heard that voice too. It sounds eerie, like an old woman whispering into the wind. Can't you hear the sound of bangles? Fading in and out. There. It happened again. Can you hear the bangles jangling? I guarantee you, whoever's behind is no human being.'

I did not stop or even bother to turn my head. I knew in my heart this voice was not of this world.

'Rea, pick up your pace. Dusk is a time when spirits and other-worldly elements are most active. Many people in the hills have had supernatural encounters while roaming the lonely streets at sunset. Specifically at odd hours of the night.'

Knowing this, we continued on our path, paying no heed to the voice. With every step, the eerie voice kept calling out to me, louder and louder. Sometimes it would whisper in our ears and sometimes it seemed to come from a distance. I had chills down my spine but continued to walk. I heard the crunching sound of leaves; the road was otherwise quiet with just our loud heartbeats. The strange voice kept following us down the winding road, relentlessly. With each bend, I was tempted to see who was calling out to me, but my strong subconscious voice kept me from turning around. If Praj had not been walking with me that day I might have just looked back. Luckily, she made sure that I kept my eyes glued straight ahead on the road.

'Praj, can you still hear her voice? Why is she hell-bent on following us? What do we do?' I whispered, absolutely stunned.

'Just keep walking, Rea. Do not turn around and do not run. I have heard of voices following people at night and we should not pay attention to it. It is freaking me out but we have to stay calm. Put up a brave face and get home first. Then we can unravel this mystery.'

I agreed to her plan and held Praj's hand tightly while increasing our pace. It had been fifteen minutes and the voice continued to call my name. It was the most haunting feeling I had ever experienced. Suddenly, the street lights looming over us began to flicker. It happened again, and then again until it went off completely. I paused for a second to catch my breath, but I was left standing in the dark. The only question that kept popping up in my head was *when will this road end and when will we see some humans? Why is this happening to me? Oh goodness! This walk feels never-ending today.*

'Rea, keep going. We are nearly there,' Praj said, chanting her prayers out loud while the voice from the forest kept getting louder by the second. It was a clash of energies. A few minutes later, I could finally see the finishing line. The gate of The Elgin. I wanted to throw my heavy bag in the corner and make a run for it, but I kept my pace steady. Like a soldier moving forward in battle.

We were home.

It seemed as if the gates of safety were a stone's throw away. Praj and I grabbed hold of each other's arms tightly and walked together, our feet in sync, like the steady beat of a drum. Suddenly, we heard the voice again.

'Reeeaa!' A prolonged call.

My heart was beating faster and faster as we moved closer to The Elgin's gates. Thank goodness Praj too was hearing the same voice or I would have thought that I was going crazy, hearing voices out of nowhere. At least, I had an alibi.

We reached the edge of the gate and finally ran into our safe haven. This was the moment when I finally turned around. I was in my own territory now. The tigress in me awoke, brimming with confidence.

There was no one behind me. Not till the very end of the

long road. It was absolutely silent and empty. Just dry leaves scattered on the lonely road. The strange voice vanished into the misty streets.

I was startled, yet I was not surprised to see no human in the flesh following us. I asked the guard at the gate if he had seen anyone following us from afar, and he too said that he had not seen anyone except Praj and me walking from the distance on Bishop's Road. My guard kept an eye on us for a long time since he had spotted me coming uphill from afar.

'What is the matter, Madam? Is everything all right?' the guard asked, looking down the long road.

I stood there in silence and said, 'Yes, everything is all right. I had a strange feeling that someone was following me.'

The guard left, bewildered, and I shut the large gates behind me as I looked down the lonely haunted road. I knew that there was something definitely mysterious in the air that evening. I would check the lunar calendar when I got back to my suite. This alignment of the sun and moon seemed to affect the veil between the worlds; All Hallows' Eve was around the corner. It was time to retreat into my sacred space and ignite my altar.

It was time to cleanse my energy. Lavender sage shifted the tense day into a healing night. I had felt and heard an unknown voice calling out my name, repeatedly, till the very moment I stepped through the gates. It had been a chilling encounter—one that I will never forget. Never turn around when you hear strange whispers in the forest. It is a lesson I have learned the hard way. I lit a white candle, charged with mantras, and placed it on my sacred altar.

'Shield me, protect me from danger. I ignite a dome of defence around me,' I said into its rising flame.

THE ATTIC AND THE GROTTO

Darjeeling is home to ancient stone buildings, like churches, libraries, schools and hotels. It can be beautiful yet haunting, which depends entirely on mood and perspective. Each building has a strong history and a unique tale to tell through its rich architecture and meaningful design. One such magnificent beauty is Loreto Convent; its attic has been our home for many years, quietly disclosing its secrets to us, one at a time, leaving us astonished. This two-hundred-year-old edifice speaks volumes. Its towering pillars make us feel comforted, yet we never know what is present within these huge halls as there is a sense of comfort mixed with unease, like a sweet and sour candy bursting in my mouth with its changing flavours.

One rainy afternoon, in the month of July, we were huddled in the attic, waiting for it to stop raining. The gusty winds crashed against our windows while the torrential rains drummed on the slanting roofs; it was a mesmerizing sight. It was 3.13 p.m. on the grandfather clock. The wind was swirling in through an open window, bringing with it droplets of rain. All the other girls had already gone back home to escape the cold and our group of four were the only ones there. We were chatting and snacking on some instant noodles. One feels hungry in the cold, and the only way to get rid of the cold is by feeding ourselves.

Outside, it looked like the evening came in early that day. As I was lost in the stormy clouds, my professor approached the four of us—it was Sir Tom. 'Hello, girls. Hiding from the rain, I see. Do not worry, the strong showers will turn into a drizzle soon. You just need to be patient. The school gates will close any time now. In about twenty minutes. Keep a check on that,' saying all that, Sir Tom quickly walked down the flight of steps. My friend Farhat, who was looking outside, suddenly screamed out loud.

'Is that Sir Tom? Oh my God! That is him—standing outside the sweet shop. How is this possible? He was right here a second ago. No way on earth he could have made it that far uphill this fast.' We rushed towards the other window to see for ourselves. It was Sir Tom. In the flesh. He was standing outside, wearing a striking blue sweater. 'Girls, but Sir Tom was wearing a brown sweater while talking to us a second ago,' I whispered into the empty and cold attic, my face losing its colour.

'If this is Sir Tom, then who was that man here?' Farhat questioned as a bolt of lightning struck following her words. The rains grew heavier with each thunderstrike; we screamed in shock and ran down the flight of steps, quicker than lightning. We did not stop, even for a minute, till we reached the grotto near the main gate. Panting and drenched in the cold rain, we did not even bother to open our umbrellas or grab our raincoats. I did not dare turn my head around. We were frightened to the core. As though we had been hit by lightning ourselves. Mother Mary's Grotto seemed to be the only safe place. So we let our instincts take over.

Sharon had led the run—the first person to put on her running shoes—and she suddenly stopped to catch her breath. Praj, Farhat and I paused at the Grotto to catch our breath when something baffling happened. Finally, we were in a safe zone.

'Girls, what is going on today? Did you see what my eyes just revealed to me?' I said, rainwater running down my pale face and goosebumps rising all over my damp skin, shaking and shivering. A dozen white candles were lit at the altar of Mother Mary. Suddenly, one of them was extinguished by the wind—only to rekindle immediately.

'The candle blew out for a few seconds and suddenly reignited on its own. Literally out of thin air,' Sharon said, joining her hands together in prayer. Shaking in the cold and with fear, Praj finally spoke with a straight face, 'I don't think it is possible for a flame to ignite like that in this pouring rain. The chances are bleak.' This time, we screamed together and ran out of the convent gates With every lightning strike, we moved a little bit faster. The whole day was too much for our minds to apprehend.

'What in heaven's name is going on?' I asked the girls as we tried to find our way in the lashing rain. The romantic weather soon turned into a haunting one. Sharon, while trying to keep pace with us in her grey pleated skirts, said, 'The convent has scared the living daylights out of me. Girls, I am sure you are aware of this particular local saying. If not, then hear me out. In the northeastern Himalayas, it is believed that lightning creates a gap between worlds. When the dark skies are full of these lightning bolts, a strong energy field is created. An energy that can be a doorway between realms and other dimensions of the universe.'

I was compelled to accept the possibility of the unknown. We felt it strongly that day. The energy of the place was one of strange vibrations and peculiar occurrences. Somehow, the events that had taken place during then are inexplicable, mysterious and other-worldly. Indra, the lord of thunder, the gatekeeper of different realms, had made his presence felt among us. I sensed his strong indigo aura surrounding us that day.

41

THE HIDDEN JEWEL

The Himalayas have hidden treasures scattered all around their lap. Its vast expanse is full of wonders that can transform our energy. Aanyaa and I call it 'increasing our vibration'. Just like shining light onto a prism splits the white light into rainbow hues, the variations of our inner journey outweigh the conquest of the highest peaks of the snow-white Himalayas.

The sacred Khecheopalri Lake, also known as the 'Wishing Lake', is about a two-and-a-half-hour drive from the quaint town of Pemayangtse. A hidden jewel awaits my presence in West Sikkim. The drive is picturesque, as flamboyant oak forests greet me on either side of the Himalayan roads. While many just casually pass by these spectacular natural wonders, without knowing or caring about their existence, I am someone who is drawn to these.

My journey to Khecheopalri Lake commences as we stop at an obscure pathway within a vast forest. I venture into a wild walkway, leading straight into the deep forest, which takes around twenty minutes through the coniferous trail. There are natural wonders lying in wait for us offbeat travellers. During this walk, I see baby pink wildflowers, countless butterflies with varied designs flying in marvellous formations and chirping sparrows building their nests on treetops. The large leaves falling from the towering trees feel magical, while the pathway takes me deeper into the forest, where something extraordinary is lying in wait for me.

I get lost in the beauty of the walk itself with the strong breeze whispering in my ears. An orchestra of rare Himalayan birds soon transforms into the sound of a gushing waterfall that is crashing into the slippery rocks below; from a distance, it looks like layers of milk falling from a height. *A vantage point for the Roman Goddess Iris*, I am deep in thought as the rays of sunlight peep in through the canopy of trees and gently touch the clear water, creating the most beautiful rainbow hue. It truly is a sight to behold. My middle-aged chauffeur knows every inch of this forest, and calls out to me from a distance, 'Over here, Rea Madam, follow my trail. Watch my steps as I move forward. This is not it.'

I watch as he moves like a swift snake through the tall grass, his long stride eating up the distance. 'Slow down, Dorjee. I cannot keep up with your pace,' I murmur, rolling up the sleeves of my pink quilted jacket. 'Seriously, Dorjee? Are you telling me there is more to this adventure?'

Showing me the way, he replies in a polite yet excited voice, 'Yes, Madam. Much more!'

I observe him quietly kneeling with his head bowed down at the base of the waterfall. I realize he is doing this gesture as a sign of respect to his natural deity—a Himalayan way of life. He then moves in silence, heading straight towards the waterfall. I follow his footsteps, jumping slowly from one rock to the other, grabbing the larger boulder in front of me through the shallow pool of rippling water. As I head into the waterfall, the clear water lets me glance into its depths; its slender fish, especially the tiny guppies, swim around my feet, almost touching me. The water seems to reflect the blue sky above, making me feel as though I am walking in the skies. I feel like I am jumping in the air amidst the countless fluffy clouds while maintaining my balance on the slippery rocks under my feet. It seems like a union of three powerful elemental bodies—the earth, water and sky, each embracing the other. I sense a oneness with the cosmic force I find myself in. Suddenly, the illusion of separation—from the elements around us and one another—has vanished.

What lies up and what lies down? I question my seeking mind.

In the meantime, while I am lost in the magic of my surroundings, I notice my chauffeur disappear through the narrow side of the mighty waterfall. I quickly snap out of my mind and get back to the present.

Where did he go? I think to myself as a water droplet falls on my face. The steady sound of water grows louder and louder as I move forward. I notice a sly opening at the corner of the waterfall and see Dorjee. I follow him through this narrow route.

'Oh, how you tease me.' I feel vulnerable in nature's wet embrace.

I cross wild plants, find my way through clusters of dry leaves and discover something out of this world. A secret waterfall awaits me, one even more mesmerizing than the one I just crossed on my way here. Its twin sister's base is covered with orange blossoms while the still waters create a gentle pool. The mesmerizing Kanchenjunga range stands tall in the background, spreading her wings of snow over the waterfall. I have just stepped into uncharted territory, like an explorer who stumbles onto something yet untouched by mankind. I hear the forest come alive through the chirping sounds of its inhabitants. This wild terrain is full of squirrels sipping from the clear water pools. I try to follow them but they quickly disperse upon my sudden arrival.

The freshwater pool has a lush green environment with the flame of the forest flowers surrounding it. Pink angel trumpets bloom freely in this wild landscape, filling the forest with their sweet fragrance. Its beauty is a deceptive illusion in these high Himalayas. I reach out towards a flower, only to be stopped immediately by my chauffeur. 'Rea Madam, do not be drawn to its pendulous petals and fragrance for it can be quite fatal if you consume it by mistake. This beautiful flower has a notorious reputation for causing hallucinations and stomach ailments. I suggest you to be careful with it. Simply enjoy its fragrance without touching it.' Amidst this wild basket, I try to make sense of nature's patterns. The angel's trumpet usually consists of five petals. *Numbers are the language of the universe*, I say to my inner being. Meanwhile, a pine cone floats on the clear water, drifting towards me, as though it is coming to the shore. Its intricate structure is in sharp contrast to the angel's trumpet, yet is stamped with its creator's unique signature. Lost in the natural world, I gaze at my reflection in the pool when a little winged forest dweller flies right towards me. This tiny daredevil has come to inspect my unannounced arrival. Its petite structure, with the hue of a blazing fire, mesmerizes me. The Himalayan fire-tailed sunbird spreads its scarlet wings while raising its sharp beak towards the open sky, like a gatekeeper about to blow their trumpet.

I want to stay at this hidden gem for a longer period of time, but we have to continue our journey towards the Wishing Lake. At that moment something serene overcomes me, and my attention drifts towards the delicate pearl ring I am wearing on my index finger. I close my eyes, take off the pearl and slip it into the depths of the freshwater pool before taking the final step out of this paradise. It is my parting gift to this waterfall.

'Till we meet again,' I whisper to the waterfall. Pearls belong in water and I sent it back to its element. I have the exceptional opportunity of naming this surreal place and want to call it 'The Two Sisters' after the unbreakable bond between my sister Aanyaa and me. It reminds me of our sacred bond and our distinct nature. Both waterfalls display a unique personality, and yet are connected to each other, sharing their lives together. Much like ours. Aanyaa reminds me of the large waterfall with the rainbow that I associate with Goddess Iris, while I am the smaller hidden one, staying lost within the embrace of the lush canopy of the forest, sharing the same space and source of life. The waterfall of the two sisters has been revealed to us—a physical manifestation of our non-human form.

42

WANDERING INTO THE WISHING LAKE

'Since ancient times, it is believed that water holds memory. Water has wisdom in its molecules. It is the giver of life, holding countless secrets in its cool depths. This is one of the reasons why a number of waterbodies are considered sacred in India and around the world,' Mr Diamond says while pouring a glass of spring water for himself, right up to the brim. 'My darling, the benefits of water are countless. It plays an important role in our physical body as well as our astral self. Let me tell you a fascinating fact about our land. This will leave you wondering for a while at least. Let's flow with the Himalayan rapids today, shall we?'

The Himalayan rivers are older than the peaks themselves. Snow never melts in our Himalayan home, giving it the name of the house of snow. Like the creation of our world, water is the first element to unfold. Overlooking the majestic Mount Pandim, I slowly sip the spring water, imagining its origin from these white peaks.

'My dear, Pemayangtse is surrounded by sacred waterbodies that will catch your interest and help you align with its energy. As the entire family is here, you should take a trip to Khecheopalri Lake—the abode of Goddess Tara. She is the Tibetan Goddess of magic, beauty and wisdom. This lake will captivate you in her divine beauty, thus awakening the subconscious light within.' My father guides me to the sacred lake with such ease. I already feel the divine in the soft breeze.

'Rea, how about a little clue...maybe a prophecy? Look through the keyhole of your soul and peek into the world. We are all united, and may the pure of hearts be allowed to gaze through these serene magical waters. This is the prophecy. The ancient myth of Khecheopalri Lake is a fascinating one that will draw you towards her depths. Legend has it that two large magical shells fell from the heavens on Earth, landing at this very spot. Then out sprung water from the dry ground, forming a clear lake. It is an oasis for the mountain people of West Sikkim. A holy site where Goddess Tara resides. According to ancient beliefs, the lake is a manifestation of the Goddess herself. A learned monk had a vision of Goddess Tara sitting on a divine lotus at the centre of the lake—a lotus of golden hue, which submerged into its depths. This lake has a powerful aura around it. There are stone pathways with steep edges to take you towards a surprise—a view like no other. The uphill climb is for about half an hour, surrounded by cherry trees. You can reach this high ground by following the numerous arrows drawn on the rocks throughout the path to guide you. Let the sacred lake reveal herself,' saying this, my father lays out the map for me. It is time to call my partner in crime for this quest. I head straight to my sister; after all, Aanyaa and I have an adventure to look forward to.

The very next morning, we make our way to Khecheopalri Lake, having received a calling from Goddess Tara. Both sides of the pathway are dotted with pretty pink cherry blossoms, with white Buddhist prayer flags dancing in the strong winds. I already feel as if nature is welcoming us.

'Aanyaa, there is a secret to this sacred space. The lake takes the form of a large footprint, which is believed to be of Goddess Tara herself. I can sense strong feminine energies swirling around, reflected by the divine and compassionate aura of the lake. Just by gazing into the calm water, I feel the warm embrace of the female Shakti. Do you sense it too?'

As we walk towards the lake, we pass a Buddhist monastery where only female monks (bhikkunis) are allowed to reside and perform rituals. I light two white candles in the holy shrine and offer the customary Buddhist prayers taught to me by Jethi. Standing shoulder to shoulder, my sister and I synchronize our prayers—our posture straight, we face the resident deity and let the monastery carry us into its divine realm. We then prostrate ourselves on the floor. We follow these steps two more times. It is a form of prayer that allows one to fully surrender to the divine and is a means of renouncing the human ego to God.

We walk on the uneven pebbled road and pass dainty white pagodas on the way to the lake, looking up at the mighty oak trees forming the path ahead. Large prayer wheels welcome us into this serene space. It is a custom to move these prayer wheels with the palm of your hands as one walks towards the holy shrines. Prayers are written on the wheel and they energize the surrounding space by creating movement as one rotates these wheels in a clockwise direction. Feeling connected to the cosmos, I let its energy flow through me, moving my wheel of fortune. After a short and calm walk on the cobbled pathways, we arrive at our destination. It feels more like our destinies as the magical wishing lake unveils itself to us.

Its water is clear as glass and appears as blue–green as turquoise. The smell of wet earth blends with the smell of the forest. Algae float on its corners, leaving the rest of the lake flawless. I feel my energy lighten with that of the lake. Butter lamps comfort my soul with their heady aroma, making me feel at home. To my utmost surprise, there is not a single leaf floating on the lake's surface, even though it is surrounded by a lush green forest with towering trees in all directions that are in full bloom.

In the distance, I notice a young bhikkuni, her prayer beads calmly sitting on the bank of the lake. I slowly walk up and stand quietly beside her, trying not to disturb her meditative state. But she senses my presence and slowly opens her eyes to look up to me.

I see such peace in her hazel-brown eyes. It is almost intoxicating.

I take a moment and speak with her. She is the best person to provide information about the lake. I say in Nepali, 'Namaste. Can I ask you a few questions to assuage my curiosity? My name is Rea and I live in Pemayangtse. I am wondering about this lake's sheer beauty. How is it possible that there is not a single leaf on the lake?'

I stand at the edge of the turquoise lake. The bhikkuni remains quiet for a moment and then says, 'You are an observant girl. The magic of nature is responsible for this. We humans can only understand what our receptors allow us to absorb. The birds from the forest come and pick up every little leaf that falls onto the surface.'

I am amazed by her answer. I am unable to believe it but then witness it for myself. She whispers, 'Look... A sparrow is gliding towards the lake.'

My eyes move with the sparrow's wings. I look carefully in the distance and witness the most magical thing ever. My logical mind cannot believe it, but the sparrow sweeps through the lake, picks up a large green leaf, brings it towards land and gently places it on the lakeside pathway. The sparrow's actions stir a strong sense of belief within me.

'Now girls, make a wish. This sacred lake is known throughout the land for fulfilling one's wishes,' the bhikkuni says, a serene smile appearing on her pale face. I close my eyes, make a wish and believe that it will come true.

Aanyaa and I have come here with a specific purpose in mind. I feel the divine energy of the place enveloping us. So we go ahead and make our wish. Our Tibetan terrier Pasha is gravely ill, following a paralytic attack. The only part of his body that he can move is his head, with his beaming eyes looking straight into ours. We need a miracle. Aanyaa's black and white terrier is not just her companion but her spirit animal.

'My Pasha is my spirit guide. His energy is the only thing that soothes my restless mind and spirit. You know Rea, when I hold Pasha in my arms, and he stares at me with his button eyes, I feel the compassion and wisdom… In his past life, he must have been a human being. I am glad that his past life's karma got him to me. I cannot imagine living in this world without him; I hope he recovers soon, Rea. I really do. I pray with my whole heart for Pasha's good health from the wish-fulfilling lake.'

I can sense her pain as though it is my own. 'I cannot see you like this, Aanyaa. I just can't bear it. My heart breaks each time I see you in pain. Life on earth is full of suffering; I wish the whole world could be rid of it. I have a hard time dealing with loss but remind myself to have hope. Pasha and you have a bond of true love…the timeless human–canine relationship…one between two souls. I feel your pain, but always remember I am here for you…forever…no matter what life brings. You will always have me.'

We hold hands and pray silently. For a minute, my mind goes blank as I seek out the voice of Goddess Tara. This moment changes the way I look at the world. It transforms me as I pray for Pasha's speedy recovery. We ask the Goddess of the lake for the most precious thing in the cosmos—time—for our innocent little terrier.

As we are in the middle of our prayers, another Buddhist bhikkuni arrives. With her calm ocean blue eyes and heavy voice, she says, 'Hello there, Tashi Delek. I was watching the two of you walking through the forest. You remind me of my elder sister back home in the village. I miss her dearly. I don't think you know this, but you are standing in one of the most sacred parts of Sikkim. If you have been summoned here by the water Goddess then there is a purpose to it. Local legends say that Sikkim's topography is divided into four plexus, each part representing the human body. Where we are standing now is the thorax, the village of Yuksom represents the third eye, Pemayangtse is said to be the heart and Tashiding the head.'

The bhikkuni continues, 'When you meditate in these sacred places of the Himalayas you are blessed into following the divine light and moving away from this mundane world created by mankind. Here, no greed, no temptation that binds one to earthly pleasures of the senses exists. It is a pure connection to the cosmos. A bridge that connects you to the Almighty. Many gurus and masters have come to these sacred places for solace. Some have even reached their ultimate destination of achieving nirvana or enlightenment. It is said that these gurus scatter their teachings in these mountains' etheric plains, which are known to be located in a different realm that can be reached through dhyana. If your mind is still and empty of thoughts, you can tap into the yogic teachings that are floating in this Himalayan wind. It's something truly out of this world. You can see many gurus meditating in this region, who are tapping into the unlimited source of knowledge that is open for anyone who wants to seek it.'

Giving us this rare piece of information, the bhikkuni begins to walk away from us, humming the prayer 'Om Mani Padme Hum' while running her hazel beads through her dainty fingers.

She leaves Aanyaa and me wondering about her words and compels us to string together the similarities in our modern lives. My sister, an expert at connecting with angels, puts forward her musings.

'Rea, don't you feel Akashic records are similar to a Wi-Fi connection in our technologically advanced world? It is invisible yet it's everywhere. Akasha holds an immense amount of data and knowledge that is unlimited. Astral records of higher wisdom by past saints and gurus are floating all around us. The only difference is that instead of connecting to a computer system, we can connect our minds with Akasha (the realm of unending knowledge) by emptying our minds of thoughts through meditation. This mystical lake is a chalice of such records in aqua form; wisdom flows through its waves. This is one of the most advanced notions I have ever come across in these hills. It leads me to conclude that ancient gurus have been practising something way more advanced than what we hold important today as per modern technology.'

We stand in silence by the sacred lake and absorb the bhikkuni's words of wisdom, to carry them with us into our daily lives. As we say goodbye to the glittering lake, tears roll down our cheeks, dropping into its turquoise waters, recording our memories. Calmness surrounds us. Aanyaa and I silently turn towards Khecheopalri Lake and the only words that come out of our mouths are, 'Till we meet again, Goddess Tara.'

43

BODHISATTVA

The Himalayas are known for their mystical nature, which sets them apart from any other mountain range in the world. It is believed that numerous beings have meditated and achieved enlightenment in the lap of these mountains. One such story of an incredible man came through the comforting voice of my Tibetan nanny, Jethi—about a bodhisattva (bodhisattvas are monks who are on the path towards bodhi or awakening [Buddhahood]).

For the longest time, Tibet's rich heritage and unique way of life remained a mystery for the rest of the world. Knowledge was passed down to Jethi by her grandfather, who had travelled the silk route from Nepal to Tibet, about the lives of saints, monks, various Buddhas that lived and continue to live today and about miracles and bodhisattvas of all kinds. The night brings with it a longing for sacred knowledge. Room Number 37 still echoes thousands of tales of wisdom and enchantments that Jethi has bestowed on us. Laying my head on her lap, her soft wrinkled hands stroking my long raven hair gently, another legend begins.

'There once lived a man called Milarepa, who had had a sad childhood. He had to face the harsh realities of life when he was young, right after his father passed away. As fate had it, his evil uncle took over the household and made his mother, sister and him servants in their own home. The young boy struggled to cope with the mental and physical torture his uncle was putting him through. So one night, he ran off into the forest to escape his misery. He lived in the dense forest for years on end and acquired tantric abilities from a monk deep in the woods. Milarepa returned home one day to find that his mother and sister had passed away in his absence while his rich uncle was thriving with his own family. He was enraged at this and vowed to take vengeance against his evil uncle who had single-handedly destroyed his happy life. With the help of his abilities, Milarepa showered large hailstorms over his uncle's house. The sudden hailstorm was so powerful that the entire house collapsed, taking the lives of his uncle, aunt and their son, along with many other people who were visiting the house. Milarepa chose a moment when a grand wedding was being held in the house; the wedding of the eldest son of his uncle was ongoing when he decided to take revenge. Soon after this vengeful act, Milarepa felt guilt and torment running through his mind. Milarepa had thought revenge would bring him peace and satisfaction but it had instead brought sleepless nights and misery.'

'He had done an evil deed by killing so many people and misusing his powers, so he went on a quest to the inner lands of Tibet in search of redemption and a guru to guide him towards correcting his deeds and his karma. Milarepa walked for months on end to look for his master—someone he had heard could guide him towards enlightenment. Milarepa finally arrived at a learned monk's doorstep and pleaded to be accepted as a student. The revered monk, named Marpa, rejected his plea several times. "Go back to your home. I will not initiate you into my teaching." Master Marpa remained as stubborn as a bull. Milarepa tried for years on end to find Marpa's acceptance, but the monk simply kept refusing his plea.

"Go home, Milarepa! You have a bag full of evil deeds. Your hands are smeared with blood of your own," the wise monk said again. "You have accumulated negative karma by misusing your powers to kill many innocent people solely for revenge. I will not show you the path to enlightenment. It takes many lifetimes to become the Buddha. I wish you would go away." But Milarepa had already decided, so Marpa gave Milarepa household chores to do as the years passed by, praying Milarepa would give up the quest. Milarepa was running out of time, and age had begun to catch up with him. He was getting older and older as the months turned into years. So he pleaded with the monk again, and this time, the wise monk agreed to initiate him. Marpa had observed Milarepa's dedication and pursuit of penance. Once the initiation was done, Milarepa went into the forest to meditate in complete isolation. During his meditation, a female spiritual messenger, a "dakini", appeared to him in a vision. The beautiful dakini showed him something very rare that he could not decipher. A sign in his dream. Curious to know the meaning of his dream, Milarepa made the journey back to his master, Marpa, and explained his vision to him, looking for some answers. However, upon hearing Milarepa's account of his dream, the learned monk Marpa was shocked. He too did not hold the answers to the questions Milarepa asked. Marpa said, "I've stumbled upon a boulder, Milarepa, while deciphering the dakini's message. I can just show you the path to enlightenment, but achieving it may require multiple lifetimes." Marpa thought about what should be done about Milarepa's vision and decided to take Milarepa to India to a greater sage who may have the answers he was looking for. Marpa and Milarepa embarked on their journey from Tibet to the Indian subcontinent and reached a small village situated between the state of Bihar and the Kingdom of Nepal. An enlightened saint heard the story of Milarepa's vision and said, "Alas! This is what I have been waiting for…" The learned guru taught Milarepa the meaning of his vision and said, "You are the man who has managed to reach enlightenment in one lifetime. This is an extremely rare occurrence." At that moment, Milarepa, who had done evil deeds in the past, became an enlightened being. The tides soon changed and Milarepa's master became his student.

'In Tibetan Buddhism, Milarepa is a highly revered master. A mortal man realizing his divinity. This is the story of how a man can change the course of his life and achieve nirvana, even in one lifetime.'

My wise governess fills my young mind with spiritual tales of enlightened beings. She goes on to say, 'Rea, our lands are one of the most blessed spaces on earth. You do not realize the magic surrounding us. We live among these sacred mountains. I will tell you something that will make you crave your own path to liberation. I am giving you a glimpse into the story of Milarepa because his footsteps lie closer to us than you think. There is a secret cave on the cliffs of West Sikkim, where Milarepa himself meditated on his path to enlightenment. It is a steep climb of roughly two to three hours from the sacred Wishing Lake (Khecheopalri). West Sikkim has magic engraved all over it. Our masters have scattered their knowledge in these Himalayas for us to tap into and download into our consciousness. These Akashic records are an open library for all to learn from. One only has to be willing to grasp its unlimited knowledge.'

44

THE THIRD EYE

'Yogic culture places importance on the concept of chakra healing and the alignment of the body with the cosmos. Vedic science shines a light on the configuration of the human body both physically and spiritually. The third eye is associated with enlightenment in most cultures in our world,' saying this, my Buddhist governess instils a unique way of life. I watch as she counts her pearl white prayer beads. Aanyaa and I are her shadows, and we definitely move like one, following her spiritual path. Jethi's deep voice addresses us.

'Girls, the third eye is located at the centre of our foreheads. Envision a ray of white light piercing through it. When our third eye is activated, our mind reaches ultimate wisdom— the universal truth—through self-awareness. Feel the energy revolving around inside your head, like a wheel chakra. Maintain its momentum. Now, envision a ray of purple, split from the white light, piercing through you. Absorb its energy into your skin. Just like the human body, our planet and the cosmos have chakras in their physical manifestations. We call it the cosmic chakra or cosmic wheel. We humans are surviving on a conscious universe that is alive in itself.' I am drawn towards these energy points and follow their call while opening a doorway to a remote town.

The first and oldest capital of the mountain Kingdom of Sikkim was the town of Yuksom, established in AD 1642.

The first ruler, Chogyal Phuntsog Namgyal, set this site as his capital, placing his coronation throne, called the 'Throne of Norbugang', in Yuksom. The geographical location of this town links it to the three sacred spots of the kingdom, giving it the spiritual name of the 'third eye' of this mountainous region. This sacred place is one of the four holy spots blessed by Guru Padmasambhava. Sikkim upholds the ideology of nirvana in its roots. Living here can draw you closer to the inner core of your being, making you abandon the material world, your soul transcending to higher dimensions. Having been brought up in this land, people are highly influenced by its nature and pick an entirely different path to live their lives to the fullest potential. This state of being comes very naturally to us Himalayan dwellers—a simple way of life, similar to the Zen way of life.

When I venture into Yuksom, at a short distance from the town of Pemayangtse, I sense a vibration that seems lighter than usual. Although it is not too far from The Elgin Mount Pandim, Yuksom makes me feel as if I'm entering a long-forgotten kingdom with historical tales embedded in its fabric.

I channel my energy, rooted in Sikkim's third eye, and gently close my eyes to focus on the pure white light at the centre of my forehead. As I follow Jethi's instructions, I sense a warm sensation on my ajna chakra, my third eye. Almost like the rays of the sun, the warmth fills the centre of my forehead and spreads through my entire body. A thought comes sailing through these mountains towards me, like a message from my spirit guides.

Rea, let the energy of Sikkim's all-seeing third eye guide you towards awakening your own. The strong smell of butter lamps surrounds me as I watch my father indulging my mother with historical tales.

'Nimmi, let me take you into the enchanted realm of Sikkim. Yuksom literally translates to "the meeting point of the three wise lamas". These three holy monks from Tibet played a key role in establishing the Sikkimese kingdom by giving the title of "Chogyal" and appointing Phuntsog Namgyal as the first religious ruler. The name Yuksom in itself holds a significant historical connection to the land. It reminds me of the tales of the three wise men in Eastern traditions.'

My mother, an expert with numbers, begins to connect the dots as my father walks her down this historical path. 'You are right, Diamond. The number three is the number of creation. The universe has its own language, my love. Numbers can act as a key or even a gateway to decipher the code of the cosmos.'

Just then, my father sees a flower with three petals. 'Nimmi, it just clicked in my mind that the number three holds a special significance in the world's religions, numerology and science. What a strange connection. According to Christian beliefs, the number three represents the father, son and the holy spirit. In Hinduism, it represents the trimūrti or the trinity of supreme divinity, Lord Brahma, Vishnu and Mahesh, in whom the cosmic functions of creation, preservation and destruction, respectively, are personified. In scientific contexts, the basic building block of all matter—the atom—consists of three basic types of subatomic particles—electrons, protons and neutrons. Then there's the natural world, comprising of water, sky and earth, followed by the ultimate triad of our beginning, end and the 'in between'. The long and steady rule of the Chogyal also collides with the number three. Their reign lasted over a period of 333 years. Three is a number that is very mysterious in nature. Here, at Yuksom, I could not help but notice a similar significance of the number.'

I join my parents' numerical conversation, adding a few drops of wisdom of my own.

'Papa, the number three is an angelic number. It's also a very magnetic number and represents the mind, body and soul. Numbers have a world of their own. Many names of people as well as places are determined by deciphering their numbers, which is a common practice in India. Numerology is an ancient science in our culture. Do you know each place in Sikkim is given a name that holds a strong connection with the existence of the town? The first Buddhist monastery in Sikkim was established in Yuksom, and is called the Dubdi Monastery; it was built in the year 1701.'

The swift wind carries dry leaves with it and my cheeks feel Yuksom's cold touch. I shift my gaze towards my mortal creators to connect with the divine. 'Papa, there is more to this land. Apart from holding archaeological and religious significance, Yuksom is a geologically strategic location as it is placed in the foothills of the Kanchenjunga National Park. You know my love for adventure runs deep, and this is my next hideout. This is also the Kanchenjunga base camp for trekkers who want to venture into the mighty upper Himalayas, and it has become one of the main reasons the village of Yuksom has become an internationally acclaimed hotspot. The biodiversity of Yuksom is unlike any other, making it the biggest natural protected area in the land.'

Lost in deep thought, we take a walk through this enchanted town. My father is a treasure trove of knowledge. He points into the distance and says, 'Here, look. I found my favourite—the proud oak tree looks to be almost a hundred years old among the maple, rhododendron, silver fir, ash and magnolia. Let's see how many you can spot.' I begin to drift away as a variety of birds chirping all around the forest lead me to the old capital.

'Come along, ladies. Time for the trump card. The best part about being here among various trek routes from Yuksom is its authentic local cuisine. On the trekking route to Dzongri (4.05 kilometres), there are small huts scattered all over the sloping hills. Interacting with the locals living here makes for a soulful cultural experience, unlike any other. Mountain men have their unique way of life and they pass on their traditions to the younger generations. They are very friendly and are wonderful hosts to strangers from different nationalities. Let's see if we can also find someone who will be willing to host us and fill our growling tummies with some thukpa,' my father announces, looking at his wristwatch. We walk for a few minutes to find a gushing waterfall with a tiny wooden cottage at its feet; the local villager offers us some delicious home-cooked meals.

The smell of fire merges with the smell of earth. I get a whiff of something being cooked in butter. Our meal has been prepared with home-grown herbs, berries and mushrooms and tossed with exotic Himalayan spices. The host of the house is dressed in traditional Sikkimese attire, with a turquoise bracelet on her hand. As we are tea lovers, she has also prepared some hot Tibetan tea with yak milk. But there is a Himalayan twist to the tea as the lady adds some fresh herbs, called 'lai', and tops it with wild mushrooms to enhance the taste.

I stroll into the courtyard for some fresh air and glance at her vegetable garden. There are a large variety of mushrooms in all shapes and size. Some are flat at the top while some are round. To my surprise, growing in the far corner of the garden, I spot an unusual member among the neutral-coloured mushrooms. My eyes focus on these button-head beauties with their stunning black shade. Our Himalayan mountains never fail to tantalize my taste buds.

I walk towards the Sikkimese lady to ask her a few questions. 'Hello, Tashi Delek. What a captivating place you have here. It must be breathtaking to live here. The gushing waterfall feels transcendental. Can you tell me a little about the trekking routes that diverge from this point? I wish to go on a pilgrimage to the cave of the Gods. Do you know anything about it?'

She gazes at me as I tower above her; seated on a bamboo stool with a pair of knitting needles in hand, the Sikkimese lady begins to knit her woollens, and then she speaks softly. 'My dear. Is it the cave of the Gods that you seek? I feel as though I have lived through this scene before. Déjà vu. How surprising. Maybe the sound of this waterfall has drawn you to me. I will surely guide you to our sacred cave. The journey ahead is full of stunning falcons and hawks flying overhead in the form of spirit guides, our ancestors. They will become our wings and eyes on this dangerous route. As you walk into this snow world, you will cross a variety of pagodas with holy stones or mendangs on them. Buddhist prayers are inscribed on them to guide travellers through the upper Himalayas. Do not be fooled by her calmness, for the mountains may rage at any given moment. The cave of the Gods is a two-day journey once you enter the gates of the Kanchenjunga National Park.'

My trip to the third eye has opened up gateways to ancient natural relics, filling the pages of my mind's vast library.

45

THE RUINS OF AN ANCIENT KINGDOM

The relic hunter in me stays alive in my homeland, pushing me towards exploring wider territories. Each day arrives with new beginnings and is filled with anticipation. My quest is always on. This time, I am venturing into the lap of a forgotten dynasty.

The month of January is here. The town of Pelling is silent today, yet it wants to share some secrets with me. I gaze into the spotless sky and ask her a question. 'O Sikkim, the last Shangri-La! What secrets do you want to share with me today? I promise I will cherish them.' While I'm talking to the snow-clad Mount Pandim, my father joins me in the silent night, under the North Star. 'Rea, what has caught your attention? I see you are having a one-on-one with the snowy peaks.'

My eyes are glued to a sacred statue glowing on the other side of the mountains. A towering Chenrézig glimmers as I venture into the pages of Himalayan history. 'Papa, can you tell me something about the first rulers of Sikkim?'

My father begins to spin the silk threads of ancient times. 'My darling, our story begins during a time of kings, queens and dynasties. The Namgyal dynasty was strong, culturally rich, ecologically blessed and religiously inclined. The Chogyal was a religious king who was crowned by four holy monks to uphold Buddhist teachings and to inculcate this religious way of life in his people. Sikkim became a living embodiment of the Buddha's teachings. The people of Sikkim believed in the purity of this land and they respected nature's ecological riches. The coronation throne of Norbugang, in the serene town of Yuksom, is an embodiment of this value. The first monarch of Sikkim was crowned by three wise lamas from three different directions, namely the north, south and west. Guru Padmasambhava, a Buddhist guru, had predicted the requirement of a fourth lama from the east, and this lama was later discovered near the town of present-day Gangtok in Sikkim itself. Thus, the town of Yuksom got its name, "the meeting place of the three learned lamas". The throne, known as the Norbugang Coronation Throne, is unlike any other ancient royal seat found around the world. On my visit here, I felt a sense of calm and serenity when I saw the royal throne. To my surprise, it is situated outdoors, under a magnificent pine tree that stands the test of time. The throne is made entirely of stone and has an arch at the top. There are colourful Buddhist prayer flags fluttering in the wind, surrounding the stone throne. Khatas, Sikkimese long silk scarves offered to the Gods, are tied on the grilles in front of the throne.'

Soaking in its history, I feel a strange connection to Yuksom. It feels as if the place is calling out to me. 'Papa, I feel a strange pull from this place,' I say to him while placing a lilac cashmere muffler around my neck.

The days pass until the moment finally arrives when we are to visit the meeting place of the three wise lamas. My family and I are the only people there on our visit as it seldom has a high influx of tourists because of its remote location. It is a Himalayan relic and is kept away from crowds. We are at Yuksom to celebrate my parents' fortieth wedding anniversary. The moment I look at the ancient throne, my heart fills with positive vibrations and inner peace. Most royal thrones around the world exude an image of dominance, power and wealth, while the Norbugang Coronation Throne oozes peace, oneness with nature and simplicity. There is something unseen connecting us to our higher self here, something extraordinary. While I am trying to find the meaning behind the placement and structure of the throne, my vision moves in the opposite direction. I observe something there that reassures me of the wisdom of this dynasty. The Norbugang Chorten holds soil segments and water from different parts of the land. This was meant to represent the collective consciousness of the land the Chogyal was chosen to rule over. The real riches meant not the gemstones, gold or silver but the fertile soil and the fresh water from the rivers and lakes that Sikkim is blessed with. The first Chogyal was anointed here with holy water and became a peaceful king. This speaks volumes about the dynasty of the Chogyal. The ancient stones of the throne may be mute, but they talk in languages that I am able to understand better than anything else I have ever known—a language of deeper symbolic meaning. One look at the throne of Norbugang, and you feel transported to ancient times. The mysticism in this space can be felt all around. The ambience feels charged with powerful vibrations that ring throughout the deep forest.

A short walk away from the coronation throne is an enchanting lake called Kathok Lake. This is one of the holiest lakes of West Sikkim and is named after Lama Kathok Kuntu Zangpo, who blessed the lake while introducing Buddhism in Sikkim. As we walk towards its emerald waters, we observe a group of Tibetan monks holding a prayer ceremony, chanting Buddhist mantras, with drumbeats floating in the air. With the sound of the conch shell, prayers are held for world peace as we are in the middle of a global pandemic. The new year has brought with it mass prayer sessions held for the entire world in all the holy places of Sikkim.

I gaze into the waters of Kathok Lake and speak to my mother, who is building a small pebble tower at a distance. It's custom for us—my mother places five stones in accordance with their decreasing sizes and builds a small tower. She then gathers the lake's clear water in her palms, and chants, 'Om... Om... Om Shanti', while allowing the water to gradually drip from her fingertips. 'Rea, step over the pebbles and come join me. Drop some water on these stones and make a wish. I have heard of Kathok Lake's magic. There is something sacred in this water.'

'Mama, the energetic field and vibrations near this waterbody are transcendental. I sense peace and serenity here, almost like a stillness that our busy minds crave. The air and water are so calm.

My mother comes towards me with her hands full of water from Kathok Lake. She sprinkles its healing droplets on me, places her hand on my head and blesses me by chanting the mantra, 'Om Mani Padme Hum'. My mother, following the rhythm of these mantras, slowly whispers to me. 'Rea, these holy mantras are very powerful. They cleanse the surrounding area of Yuksom and maintain the purity of this lake. I'll let you in on a secret too; I know how much you love those. This natural lake is fed by underground spring water. No matter what the season, this lake never runs dry. Just as this lake, I pray water never runs dry in your life too, my child.' Taking me in her arms, she showers me with blessings, and wraps me in a hug, showing her unconditional love. She continues, 'Yuksom's untouched beauty attracts Buddhist pilgrims from all around the globe. It is a one-of-a-kind Himalayan wonder.

Very few places in the world are left undisturbed by human interference, and Kathok Lake is a gem amidst the Himalayan wilderness. Nature lovers and spiritual seekers feel at home just by being a part of this celestial vibration—like us. If one is looking for forest therapy, auric cleansing through water or even fascinating ancient history, Yuksom is the place to be.'

∽

The Elgin Mount Pandim exudes charm; it is a forest retreat that is not only palatial but also comforting. The wild forest and the architecture of the building, with its authentic Sikkimese furniture, make one feel that they are amidst an ancient culture that is still alive within our walls and beyond it. From the moment you step through the arches of the gates decorated with dragons, right up to the artistic roof, the vibrant culture of our heritage hotel welcomes you with a warm embrace and high Himalayan spirits. Scarlet carpets are laid throughout the premises, which makes you feel like you are walking the path of the royals. The highlight of our hotel is the glittering snow on the Kanchenjunga and the playful snow on the ground, our charming mascots, Coco and Kara. My two snowballs light up The Elgin grounds, even on the dullest of days.

From the pure white happy souls, we move to darker shades of the night with Shadow and Spirit, our two stallions. They are as much a part of the Oberoi family as their human counterparts. Shadow is dark and handsome like the night while Spirit is hash brown and lively, living up to his name. Aanyaa and I ride the mountains on Shadow and Spirit, respectively. We choose our stallions with great care and attention. My father's keen eyes always pick out the perfect steed. Our family's love for horses runs deep.

The untouched forest is our Himalayan playground. Pemayangtse, in West Sikkim, is a neighbour to many historic, cultural and religious sites. My rendezvous with history begins at Pemayangtse with the ancient ruins of Rabdentse.

If you wish to indulge in history and mythology like me, the Rabdentse Ruins are the most fascinating place to bring out the explorer in you. I usually venture into this terrain either on a short hike or on a mountain bike. Aanyaa and I are drawn to these offbeat sites. Aanyaa says, 'If these ancient woods could talk, they would unfold the wisdom of the ages. I wonder how old these trees must be. Feels like I am entering a different dimension.'

The mode of transport and the journey ahead completely depend on one's preference. I walk down from the hilltop where The Elgin Mount Pandim is situated all the way to Rabdentse. The Archaeological Survey of India considers Rabdentse to be a national heritage. My sister walks with me, shoulder to shoulder, through its red rustic gates. I feel a mystery unfold as I stroll through the forest and say, 'Aanyaa, take a look at this stone tablet. It has the ancient Sikkimese crest on it. Rabdentse was the second capital of the former Kingdom of Sikkim; it's located on a ridge destroyed by the invaders from Nepal. The ruins of this ancient kingdom can transport us back into time to what once was.'

We enter the gates of the ancient kingdom and take a short hike through pathways in the forest, and I say, 'Aanyaa, with each step forward I feel like I am moving backwards in time.'

While talking to my sister, a voice in my head picks up a line of thought. *What is time after all? It is the ticking of a clock; everything eventually fades away but what remains makes history. Just like these Rabdentse Ruins.*

Through the two-kilometre-long forest tunnel, we arrive on a flatland that showcases an ancient city.

'I see a city of stone,' I tug at Aanyaa's coat. 'Look at the ancient stone throne standing in the centre of this city. These large pillars are called "chortens". How mesmerizing it is to witness the throne of the first Chogyal, the kings of Sikkim.'

We walk into the deep layers of this archaeological site. I am witnessing the alluring Kanchenjunga in the backdrop of the ruins, almost protecting this ancient kingdom of the Chogyal.

Pure white prayer flags adorn this ancient city. ' My sister tunes in to her spirit guide and leads me, saying, 'Rea, it is believed that the winds carry these prayers throughout the land, blessing each part of our little Himalayan state. Every rock, tree, ancient waterbody, animal and human alike can feel the positive vibrations created by these flags and can use them to transcend into a higher state of consciousness. It purifies the land and wards away any energy belonging to a lower frequency in the mountains. They are our astral shield.

Rabdentse has three significantly tall ancient stones, called Namphogang. These stones hold a special place in the history of Rabdentse as the seat of the ancient judges in the kingdom. The ancient kingdom had a set law and order, and judges from courts upheld the law and maintained the peace of the land. The king had allocated three supreme judges during his reign. He was known to be a just ruler throughout the land. The stone throne placed here is where the Chogyal gave audiences to the general public himself.

'Let me give you a little insight into the Chogyal's life. These ruins hide a love story behind their strong façade, Rea. Local folklore has songs of a Bhutia king and his beloved Limbu wife. King Tensung Namgyal formed Rabdentse as the capital city of his Himalayan empire and built his palace of stone to mark his dynasty. His wife belonged to the Himalayan Limbu tribe, bringing peace to the land with their union. The beautiful Limbu queen was given a special gift as a token of the king's love. The queen was asked to give it a name. The ancient name given to the land by the Lepcha tribe was "Nye-mae-el" or paradise.' Stepping into the ruins, we move further inside the ancient kingdom.

'Aanyaa, we are at the royal palace grounds where the king would be stationed with his army. Take a look at these marked religious sites where the royal family would perform religious ceremonies.'

This open space, with its glorious mountains and ancient stone pillars, has a mysterious vibration to it that words cannot do justice to. As I am taking a break at this spot, lying on the grass, soaking in its ancient positive energy, I notice another person in the distance—probably the only other person there apart from us. An old Sikkimese man is sitting under the ancient throne, looking for something in the grass.

'Aanyaa, well, finally I can see another face.' I break the silence while walking towards him.

'Tashi Delek.' I wave at the old man in a friendly manner. 'What are you looking for in the grass with such determination?' Aanyaa asks, beginning a conversation with the old Sikkimese man.

'I am looking for a four-leaf clover. I use it as an offering at the nearby shrine. I cannot seem to find even one today. Can you girls help me?' says the old man, gazing at us with innocence.

'Yes, surely we will help you.' I quickly begin to look into the never-ending grass strands. Some time goes by, and then suddenly, Aanyaa shouts from a distance, 'I found it! Look, I found it.'

We let out a sigh of relief and so does the old man. 'Thank

you for this leaf. Why don't you come with me to the Buddhist shrine? Because we found this together, we should offer it together too.'

The kind old man then becomes our guide, leading us to a small lane that takes us back into the forest. Ten minutes into the dark trail, we reach a quaint shrine of the Buddha with a large rock behind it.

'Rea, take a look. The shrine is cut out of the same rock. I wonder what the significance of this shrine is.' My sister turns towards the old man, who seems focused on lighting the sage in his hand. Once lit, he moves the sage around the shrine four times, clockwise.

'This shrine is hidden in these forests and only a handful of local villagers know of its existence. Seems like you two have been drawn to this shrine and I am the messenger in between. Let me take you into the realm of Sikkimese legend. This rock is not an ordinary rock formation. It is known as the "Rabdentse Dragon". Local legends speak of a dragon terrorizing a little village and destroying their livestock, creating havoc and leading to serious discussions among the villagers. Months went by, and the entire district was left hopeless and in despair. Urgent help was needed, and help did come. One evening, through the storm, a learned man came from the far north and destroyed this terrorizing dragon with his sword, cutting it into two pieces and turning it into stone. Freezing it forever so it may never create panic again. This large rock is the upper body of the Rabdentse Dragon. His fierce face with fiery eyes turned into cold stone. A Buddhist shrine was made at this spot to protect the land from unforeseen dangers in the future, sealing the dragon forever.'

'Come, young ladies, let's make our offering while the light still illuminates our path. The forest will turn dark soon.'

My sister, the old Sikkimese man and I hold onto the delicate four-leaf clover and place it gently on the shrine. We tie a white khata silk scarf on to a small rock, right under the shrine, and let the wild energy of the forest take over. With my bare feet on the wet grass, I feel connected to Mother Earth. Its soothing energy leaves us in wonderment, lost among the ancient Rabdentse Ruins.

Will the dragon awake again? Both of us are left toying with the question.

46

THE MAGNIFICENT KANCHENJUNGA

Our shield and our protector, the mighty Kanchenjunga is considered sacred by the local tribes living in its foothills. With the winter solstice around the corner, the longest night of the year is celebrated with a bonfire, blueberry pie and hidden knowledge ready to be unravelled.

'And now it begins. Lady Winter sends in her dark knight to announce her annual arrival,' I say to the mountains. Dressed in the colours of winter, I hold a lemongrass-scented candle. The night is of renewal and rebirth, and it is an auspicious time to revisit our roots. Under the starry sky of the winter solstice, I gaze upwards at the white peak of snow and ice. 'Let me take you into our Himalayan home. A place of history, mythology and romance,' I say to a lady in peach. 'The kings of Sikkim, the Chogyal, throughout the centuries forbade any climbers from reaching the summit of this holy mountain—its holy ground. To date, the summit has never been climbed by any mountaineer from Sikkim. A lot can be deciphered from a name; Kanchenjunga, also spelt Khangchendzonga, means "the five treasures of the high snow" in the Tibetan language—"khang" meaning snow; "chen" meaning great; "dzo" meaning treasure; "nga" meaning five. The treasure consists of gold, salt, precious stones, sacred scriptures and its invincible armour. This is the third-highest peak in the world at 28,169 feet above sea level. Among the Himalayan

Limbu tribe, the Kanchenjunga is called Senjelungma and is believed to be the realm of the Goddess Yuma Samang. When I gaze at the Himalayas, I sense an all-encompassing feeling. These mountains have the highest frequency of vibrations on the planet; their snow-white peaks are considered divine, having an energy spectrum like no other. For us Himalayan people, the Kanchenjunga is not just a muse of admiration but a higher dimension, connecting our consciousness to the ultimate cosmic power we call God.' I try to give the stranger a glimpse of our Himalayan soul. 'This is my home. This is life under Kanchenjunga's white wings.'

'Apart from its mystical and enticing nature, Kanchenjunga is known to be one of the most treacherous peaks in the world. Its harsh terrain and frequent avalanches make it one of the least climbed mountains on the globe. The seasoned climbers often say, "The mountain chooses the people who set foot on it and not the other way around." It is an alternate dimension on the same planet. The Chogyal of Sikkim made a promise to the mountain's holy deities that the summit shall never be climbed through their borders. Till today, mountaineers have to stop at a distance from the summit as a sign of respect. I have heard of these legends from guides who hold trekking expeditions in these mountains. They say, "Anyone who has come close to the summit has perished and has never returned from the mountains. Anyone who violates this sacred mountain is bound to lose their life in an attempt to conquer it." It is also believed that a demon resides on these mountains; the Kanchenjunga rakshasa, who lives high up the slopes, wanders about and protects the mountains. The locals call this demon *Dzö-nga*, a name adapted from the mountain itself.'

One winter night, we sat around the fireplace in the common area with glasses of brandy in our hands. My mother sat comfortably at the card table, playing a round of solitaire. The night was chilly. The mountaineers who arrived from Sikkim also joined our little party, warming up near the fireplace while popping open a bottle of Bordeaux. They were full of fire and in a mood to celebrate their recently concluded expedition. The night began with introductions and ended with a discussion on the mysteries of the Himalayas. The mountaineers shared exciting stories of their journeys into the unknown. A rugged-faced Sherpa and a group of Swiss mountaineers, who brought out their best cheese, began to share tales about this Himalayan sacred summit. The multiple lines on the Sherpa's face, right across his piercing eyes, reveal his life experiences.

Sitting under the dimmed crystal chandelier, in front of the blazing fire, the mountaineers wore frostbite and dry skin with pride. The Sherpa spoke up, silencing the buzz of conversation in the cosy room. Holding a cinnamon stick in his hand, he said, 'In 1925, a group of Britishers, who were part of a geological expedition, came across an unusual creature on the slopes of the Kanchenjunga range. They were left surprised and startled by this supernatural encounter.'

'Caught in the middle of thick snow, they came down to base camp. Filled with curiosity, they asked the local people of the village about this strange creature they had encountered on the slopes. The locals described it as the "Kanchenjunga demon".'

The story gave me the chills and I moved closer to the fire. I was swept into the mysteries of Kanchenjunga's slopes and, with my back to the flames, was listening attentively to the Sherpa, who continued to uncover Kanchenjunga's secrets with brimming confidence.

'In 1962, there was another tale that sparked conversation

and curiosity all over the Himalayan belt. It was about a Tibetan monk, named Tulshuk Lingpa, who wanted to find a gateway into a mythical land of everlasting bliss. A land supposed to be an abode of the ascended masters, also known as Shangri-La in many legends. Tulshuk Lingpa, along with his 300 followers, made his way up the mighty Kanchenjunga. They had with them their holy scriptures. The monks were chanting mantras and their voices grew louder as they went higher up the snowy glaciers. The guardian spirits of the mountains were aware of their unwanted presence. Soon, a mighty avalanche engulfed the monks...and they disappeared...forever! Their search for the hidden land of bliss came to a tragic end. The moral of the story is that unless the deities of the Kanchenjunga give way to the climbers, the expedition will never be fulfilled. Only the holiest of souls, those who are called by the mountain itself, can reach this mystical land of bliss. The gates of Shangri-La appear only to the worthy.

'I must wrap up our chilling journey by telling you yet another gripping tale based on true events. It is about Wanda Rutkiewicz who arrived from Poland to conquer the mighty Kanchenjunga. She did not believe in the superstitions and legends surrounding this sacred mountain and attempted to climb it despite multiple warnings by local mountaineers. She was a well-known climber who had successfully reached the summits of all fourteen of the eight-thousanders. This time, she set her sights on the Kanchenjunga peak and went up the dangerous slopes—daring the mountains to surrender. Days went by, and no one heard about her whereabouts. A search party was sent to look for her, but her body was never found. She vanished somewhere on the slopes of this mighty mountain. Locals whispered in the villages, "The spirits of the Kanchenjunga have been offended by her arrogance." She froze in the snow and just vanished.' This story sent chills down my spine, as though it was me who got caught in an avalanche.

'This mountain is not to be taken lightly and can prove to be very dangerous for those who do not respect its holy deities. Buddhist monks believe that this summit is of religious value to the people of Sikkim and they will not allow it to be tarnished in the name of tourism. Some mountains are not meant to be conquered by man. Instead, they are meant to be admired for their enchanting beauty and blissful presence. We believe that nature is to be respected and not dominated by mankind. If we learn to do that, then man will be at peace with his surroundings. Nature holds us in its lap, just like our mother who carries us in her womb. It is our source of life. Future generations will have to learn to coexist with Mother Nature or suffer her wrath.'

47

THE BIRD'S SONG

The chirping of exotic birds within The Elgin's grounds signals morning's arrival with the exquisite music of untamed nature. Whether it is at The Elgin in Darjeeling, Silver Oaks in Kalimpong, Nor-Khill in Gangtok, Mount Pandim in Pelling or The Elgin Fairlawn (our fifth home) in Kolkata, the birds are proudly parading everywhere. Each morning without fail at 4 a.m., our exotic birds bring in the sunrise with their anthem. Each unique species, with its different songs, floats around the atmosphere. They are nature's alarm clocks, waking us up and signalling the arrival of the day. The birdsong is mellifluous.

It is spring in the city of joy, and my winged friends are busy collecting nectar. With chilled sugarcane juice in hand, I make my way up the stairs from the garden café to the balcony that I call 'my little treehouse'. I tap into the Wi-Fi to play music when I suddenly pause to tap into something else. Chirping sounds float in the air as birds flock to the sacred banyan tree spread around the Fairlawn. I can hear house sparrows communicating with each other, accompanied by bright green parrots greeting me on my balcony. The birds are reaching out to each other from the far ends of the banyan's branches, perfectly in sync. I lie on the couch, stretch my legs and lift my hair over the cushion, spreading it like a fan. I let my skin soak in the morning sun. 'It's time for some

Vitamin D and sun-kissed look,' I think to myself, my eyes closed and my hearing magnified. I slowly begin to shift my focus to my other senses—sound and smell. I can hear Jethi's voice in my mind.

She says, 'Rea, keeping the mind still is the simplest yet hardest thing. Let me help you in your inner journey. Envision the sign of infinity taking the form of your body. Feel the inward and outward flow of energy. Feel its rhythm. Keep the energy moving between the two loops. Inwards and outwards. Only when you dig deep inside yourself, you will be able to transcend outside it. Everything is linked together, like a chain. We need to observe its pattern. The simplicity of creation.'

Time passes without me realizing it. I feel like I am meditating in nature. *How long have I been lying on this couch?* I wonder. The clock suggests it's 2.22 p.m. What? It's afternoon already! Noticing the synchronized pattern of time on my watch, I wonder if it means I am on the right path. Am I where the universe wants me to be? I am lost in thoughts, trying to decipher the code of the cosmos, when I hear a strange sound. Tap, tap, tap…

I look at the mango tree above me on the right and spot a woodpecker digging the tree trunk, its sharp beak acting like a samurai sword, cutting through the solid wood. Breakfast time on the balcony at The Elgin Fairlawn can mean that guests from the bird kingdom frequently accompany you, chirping and fidgeting on the edges. The mighty banyan tree is as wise as its years, and it is home to a variety of our winged friends nesting in its vast embrace. There is an entire ecosystem in there. I gaze at the bodhi tree to feel a whisper in the air. I hear Jethi's voice speaking through its branches and her face emerges from the trunk. The ancient banyan shapeshifts into my wise Buddhist nanny and starts narrating a tale of two men.

'There once were two men. Two extremely religious and pious men. Their two worlds collided when they met. Soon, a battle of spiritual supremacy began. The two men started to argue and debate endlessly, thereby leading to a challenge. The two decided to pray to their Gods while crossing a raging river. Whoever made it to the other side would be the victor. The one with a pure soul. The date was set for the day after tomorrow. Dispersing immediately, the two men began their preparations. The man named Tul began his cleansing ritual. He vigorously rubbed and scrubbed his body and chanted prayers for the entire two days. Tul cleansed his body with milk and purified his surroundings with herbs. He washed his clothes and didn't touch even a grain of rice. Tul was ready for the challenge. In contrast, his competitor, Sal, was still occupied in his preparations. Sal retired into a small, dark room in his house and drifted into deep meditation. Not budging from his fixed spot, Sal did not even eat or drink. He did not move an inch till the judgement day arrived.

'Tul and Sal met on the banks of the raging river, prepared for the challenge. Tul gazed at Sal from head to toe and clicked his tongue in mock disapproval. "You are covered in mud, my friend! Your clothes are torn and tattered at the edges. The Gods will not be pleased with you." Sal ignored his remark. He took some water and splashed it on his muddy face. The face-off commenced! The two men joined their hands in prayer and walked into the river side by side. Strong currents came their way, moving them from left to right, but the two determined men kept walking. Sal closed his eyes and walked straight through the centre of the river and felt its currents ebb away. Sal opened his eyes to find himself standing on the other side of the river. He passed the test. He let out a sigh of relief. Sal turned around to spot his competitor, but all that lay in front of him was the gushing river. Tul had vanished! The river had placed her judgement. 'The man of pure heart shall pass through.'

∽

I feel wisdom diffused in the air and catch a whiff of frangipani. Among all our hotels, The Elgin Mount Pandim is especially known for its various species of exotic Himalayan birds. These rare birds are only found in the western part of Sikkim. Because the hotel is built in the middle of a conserved forest of seventeen acres, the sound of wildlife comes straight through my bedroom windows. The birds sing songs of the land. The vast forest is home to these chirping delights, which is every bird watcher's paradise. I take hold of a pair of binoculars and sit by the rolling gardens to spot these little creatures in their natural playground.

'This is our home now.' The thought swiftly comes to my mind as I gaze at the open skies.

Ornithologists will have a field day at The Elgin Mount Pandim. I too have to try my hand at it. Looking out for a while, I spot a Himalayan bulbul. I watch as it flies past me with its petite indigo wings. I have no time to even take my phone out to capture the moment. It flies swiftly into the crimson sky. I turn towards the left to notice my energetic Coco chasing tiny sparrows as they land on the lush grass. Coco is single-handedly responsible for driving all the sparrows away. He also finds it thrilling to chase the endangered red pandas right into their bamboo forests. The poor little pandas! They have learned to keep away from the grounds. Russian Samoyeds can be extremely territorial when it comes to other animals entering their domain and can be great friends to have in this open wilderness.

'Coco! Come here, boy! Come here! Stop annoying the

little birds!' I call out to my fluffy white snowball. Hearing my voice, Coco quickly gives me a guilty look and puts his head down on the grass. I wish I could have spotted a few more birds, especially the rare black-throated sunbird. Let's see what the day brings. I frequently explore our natural habitat. Some other exotic species that can be found within this diverse landscape are the red-faced liocichla, fire-tailed myzornis, scarlet finch, black-headed shrike-babbler, blue-fronted redstart, Indian white-eye, spot-winged grosbeak, blue whistling thrush, green-backed tit, stripe-throated yuhina, grey bush chat, whiskered yuhina, white-capped water redstart and many more.

My father, on the rounds of his beloved garden, imparts some much-needed knowledge about the forest. 'Rea, if you are lucky enough, you can maybe spot a yet undiscovered species. We attract a variety of discoverers who come deep into these Himalayas in search of natural wonders. While some are looking to discover the high snow-clad peaks, others want to search for native species of the animal kingdom, including Himalayan black bears, shy snow leopards, barking deer and our beloved red pandas. There are yet others who want to get lost in the history of the land while some want to document its unique culture. Some people are looking for deeper meaning in life through meditation and religious devotion while others want to discover themselves. Our guests are often those who come here to spend time with nature in one way or the other, making The Elgin their home away from home. They become a part of our extended family, reaching all corners of the globe. Our guests make The Elgin what it is today. Wherever your interests lie, The Elgin makes room for growth, self-discovery, knowledge-building, adventure and spirituality.'

IN GRATITUDE

Late Mr Brij Raj Oberoi (Papa)

Mrs Nimmi Oberoi (Mama)

Ms Aanyaa Oberoi (my north star)

Mr Viraj Oberoi

Mr Zeeshan Ali

Mr Jamling Tenzing Norgay

Mr Badal Majumdar

Ms Ankhphutti Sherpa (Jethi)

Mr Dawa Lepcha

Sister Teresa

Ms Prajwalita Subba

Ms Farhat Zia

Ms Sharon Palzer